# FOUR-DIMENSIONAL SPACE

# FOUR-DIMENSIONAL SPACE

## LUDWIG ECKHART

*Translated by*

ARTHUR L. BIGELOW

*and*

STEVE M. SLABY

*Bloomington*  INDIANA UNIVERSITY PRESS  *London*

# CONTENTS

|  |  |
|---|---|
| Preface | 7 |
| Author's Foreword | 13 |
| 1. $R_1$ and its visualization | 17 |
| 2. $R_2$ and its visualization | 18 |
| 3. $R_3$ and its representation | 21 |
| 4. Position relationships and measurement | 25 |
| 5. Abstract $R_n$ | 27 |
| 6. Abstract $R_4$ | 32 |
| 7. Measurement in abstract $R_4$ | 37 |
| 8. Representation of $R_4$ | 39 |
| 9. Coordinate spaces and perpendicularity | 41 |
| 10. The projection of points in space onto the coordinate planes | 43 |
| 11. Relating $R_4$ to the drawing surface. The descriptive geometry of $R_4$ | 45 |
| 12. Lines and distances in $R_4$ | 47 |
| 13. Parallel lines | 50 |
| 14. The representation of the plane | 52 |
| 15. The point of intersection of two planes | 57 |
| 16. Assumption of particular positions of planes with respect to each other | 59 |
| 17. A theorem for three planes | 60 |
| 18. Representation of the space | 60 |
| 19. The rotation of a space around a plane | 63 |
| 20. Representation of the traces of a space | 67 |
| 21. The representation of space by the defining ray bundle (group of projection lines) | 70 |

# 6 *Contents*

22. The normals to a space   73
23. $R_4$ in relation to $\boldsymbol{R}_3$   76
24. The polytopes (multicells)   78
25. The super sphere (sphere in four-dimensional space)   81
26. Lines in $R_4$   83
27. The Einstein-Minkowski world   85
28. The materialization of $R_4$. A spherical geometry in $\boldsymbol{R}_3$   87
29. Historical notes   89
30. Bibliographical note   90

# PREFACE

The study of four-dimensional space (or four-dimensional geometry) has been greatly neglected by graphicians in this country. Its "abstractions" have caused them to look upon this higher geometry as something for the concern of mathematicians only. This state of mind has been the cause of a certain traditionalism in the field of engineering graphics, especially, and this at a time when other scientific and engineering disciplines are undergoing re-evaluation and re-orientation, the "new" atmosphere engendering dramatic new discoveries and developments in science and technology.

For almost a century now, scholars have been occupied with a geometry of several dimensions. Often they have worked independently of each other, each offering something toward a common goal which none could have imagined at the time; sometimes they have known of others' labors and have used certain of their premises in their work. In 1929 Prof. Dr. Ludwig Eckhart, lecturer at the Technische Hochschule in Vienna, published his *Der vierdimensionale Raum* (Verlag und Druck von B. G. Teubner, Leipzig und Berlin). The work is one of a number of treatises on the subject and has, with others, inspired the deeper investigation into this branch of graphics taking place at the present time.

The reason this work—in English—has been brought to the attention of the engineering graphics community is just this: to stimulate thinking in and visualization of four-dimensional space, through the medium of descriptive geometry and through this encourage research and teaching in

7

"higher" graphics. We feel that Eckhart's development introduces the graphics scholar to abstract geometrical areas which open up a fertile field for work in theoretical graphics, and believe that his presentation of "four-dimensional space" represents a fundamental approach which can be grasped by an inquiring mind and will challenge the imagination. It opens up the vista of a "space" which plays an important role in many theories of physics and which can have many applications in engineering.

We want to thank Professor Hans Winterkorn (of the Civil Engineering Department of the School of Engineering and Applied Science, Princeton University) and Mr. C. Ernesto S. Lindgren (Visiting Research Engineer with the Department of Graphics and Engineering Drawing of the School of Engineering and Applied Science, on leave from the United States Steel Corporation 1964-65) for their invaluable advice as consultants to this project. Likewise we want to express our deep appreciation to Mrs. Suzanne Fisher for typing the manuscript with great care and patience.

April 15, 1966                                   Arthur L. Bigelow
Princeton, New Jersey                            Steve M. Slaby

## Note

Arthur L. Bigelow died on February 25, 1967. His passing was a shock and a deep personal loss to me. Not only were we colleagues in graphics for many years, we were also very close friends. We shared our joys and our trials.

I am thankful for having been able to experience Arthur Bigelow's personality. He was a man whose interests were wide ranging and many faceted. In addition to his work in graphics he was world renowned in the field of campanalogy, having designed and built many carillons in this country. He also played the carillon with virtuosity.

I am also thankful for the publication of this important work, which would not have been possible without his major contribution.

September 5, 1967                                    Steve M. Slaby
Princeton, New Jersey

# FOUR-DIMENSIONAL SPACE

# AUTHOR'S FOREWORD

It is not intended here to introduce the reader to the secrets of the four-dimensional concept by purely analytical means or those of abstract geometry: rather he is given an opportunity, by way of representational procedure, to familiarize himself with it step by step and thus to acquire a clear perception of the seemingly unrepresentable. To this end, study of the text must be continuously accompanied by graphic representations, the most important of which are given in the illustrations. Only the fundamental principles of plane analytic geometry and descriptive geometry are necessary for this study.

June 4, 1929                                                    L. Eckhart
Vienna

13

# GLOSSARY OF TERMS AND SYMBOLS

$R_0 = $ A space of zero dimension  
$R_1 = $ A space of *one* dimension  
$R_2 = $ A space of *two* dimensions  
$R_3 = $ A space of *three* dimensions  
$R_4 = $ A space of *four* dimensions  
$R_n = $ A space of $n$ dimensions  
$V_1{}^2 = $ A quadratic one-dimensional space  

Linear structures

# 1. $R_1$ AND ITS VISUALIZATION

If we take a straight line and consider it as the representation of all of its points, then each of such points $P$ can be fixed by a real number $x$ which denotes how far removed $P$ is from a chosen point $O$ on the line. To eliminate any ambiguity, both positive and negative values of $x$ are allowed, which will then be assigned on both sides of $O$. Therefore for every real value of $x$ there is only one point $P$, and by this the line itself is converted to the known line of numbers. One calls $x$ the coordinate from $P$ and it is written $P(x)$; accordingly $O$ has the coordinate 0 (zero) and is called the beginning point, or origin (Figure 1). The direction of increasing values of $x$ is always denoted by an arrow.

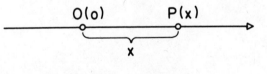

FIGURE 1

The infinite number of possible values of the variable $x$ corresponds exactly to the infinite number of points on the line, and vice versa. We can say that the number of points on the line is $\infty$ (also written $\infty^1$); because these $\infty$ possibilities have originated from varying the unique quantity $x$, we designate the line as a simple extended (one-dimensional) locus of points,

17

to which we will attach the symbol $R_1$. Correspondingly, an individual point can be designated as a zero-multiple (or a non-extended multiple) of extended space, which then can be designated, analogously, by the symbol $R_0$. Instead of saying: the line contains an infinite number of points, we can express it briefly this way: $R_1$ has $\infty^1 R_0$.* If we now consider several points $P_1(x_1)$, $P_2(x_2)$ . . . on the line, taking into account their mutual relationship, we then get a geometry of the line whose element is the point. All such geometrical relationships are equivalent to calculations with coordinate $x$; we therefore are dealing with an analytical geometry of the line. We can also free ourselves entirely from any geometrical representation if we simply designate the value $x$ as a "point"; then we are only concerned with calculations which can be expressed in geometrical language. Thus for example the "section ratio" of three "points" $x_1$, $x_2$, and $x_3$ on a line, is defined by the expression $(x_3 - x_1) : (x_3 - x_2)$; with this we can work purely abstractly; if, however, for the sake of easier visualization, we take a line of numbers, then the geometric proportion of two lengths which are defined by three points on the line viz. $P_1P_3 : P_2P_3$ will correspond to the "section ratio" of $x_1$, $x_2$, $x_3$, defined by the expression $\overline{P_1P_3} : \overline{P_2P_3}$.

## 2. $R_2$ AND ITS VISUALIZATION

If we now consider a plane as the locus of all its points, then we can define each point $P$ in the usual way by two coordinates

* Translator's note: Read: $R_1$ has an infinite number of spaces of zero dimension.

$x$ and $y$, which are drawn on a right-angle system of coordinates on this plane (Figure 2). Since we can combine every one of the $\infty$-multiple values of $x$ with every one of the values of $y$, we can define the quantity of all points $P(x, y)$ on the plane with $\infty \cdot \infty = \infty^2$. We say briefly: the plane has $\infty^2$ points and this surface is defined as a two-fold extended (two-dimensional) point space with the symbol $R_2$. An $R_2$ has $\infty^2 R_0$. The geometrical treatment is the *planimetric* (the mensuration of plane surfaces); the arithmetical treatment corresponds to analytic plane geometry. When we work in plane geometry we have the advantage of being able to follow our calculations directly by constructions on the drawing surface.

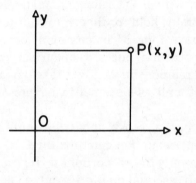

FIGURE 2

If we write an equation $ax + by + c = 0$, all points $P(xy)$, which satisfy the equation, define a straight line; this was previously indicated, in section 1, the only space available for a geometry; but now it is a component or structure in $R_2$. Naturally it also has $\infty^1$ points here, since these now depend on the value of one variable, for example $x$, and the other, $y$, is determined by the given equation; hence it is possible to designate with $R_1$ a straight line within $R_2$, which of course is apparent from observation.

The following theorems are now immediately clear: through two $R_0$ can go only one $R_1$; two $R_1$ intersect in an $R_0$.*

The equation $x^2 + y^2 = r^2$ denotes a circle which, by the same analytical reasoning as used in the case of the line, can be considered as a one-dimensional extended space. The visual difference between them lies in the form, the analytical difference in the degree of the equation. We shall therefore, for purposes of distinction, denote the circle as a quadratic—one-dimensional extended space—and give it the symbol $V_1^2$, where the subscript gives the extension and the superscript the degree. Accordingly, we could call a straight line a linear space with the symbol $V_1^1$; however, we always use the letter $R$ for linear structures (that is, those determined by linear equations). As a matter of fact, the symbol $V_1^2$ belongs to all conic sections and the following theorems hold for them: an $R_1$ intersects a $V_1^2$ in two $R_0$; two $V_1^2$ have four $R_0$ in common, etc. As we see, these theorems are nothing but a geometrical means of expressing algebraic relationships, if we take an abstract view and accept a "point" only as a geometrical expression of the number pair $x, y$.

Now we can also ask about the number of lines in the plane. The linear equation contains three constants $a, b, c$, for which however only the proportions $a : b : c$ are decisive; it thus depends on two essential quantities only (i.e., independent variables). This can be recognized at once when, for example, we give the equation the form $(a/c)x + (b/c)y + 1 = 0$. All values of $a/c$ can be combined with all values of $b/c$; hence, the plane contains $\infty^2 R_1$. Through an $R_0$ pass $\infty^1 R_1$, because if $x$ and $y$ are fixed in the linear equation, then only $a/c$ can be chosen, since $b/c$ is already determined by the equation. If we cut a sheaf of rays with a line, then we understand at once that there must be just as many lines in the sheaf as there are points on the lines, hence $\infty^1$.

* Translator's note: through two points $(R_0)$ only one line $(R_1)$ can pass; two lines $(R_1)$ intersect in a point $(R_0)$.

## 3. $R_3$ AND ITS REPRESENTATION

The relationships are even more variegated when we consider points in space in the usual meaning. If we introduce a rectangular coordinate system, then point $P$ is determined by the numbers $x, y, z$ (Figure 3). There are $\infty \cdot \infty \cdot \infty = \infty^3$ points,

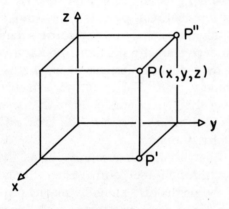

FIGURE 3

hence the space can be simply described as threefold (three-dimensional) extended space ($R_3$).

A linear equation $ax + by + cz + d = 0$ gives the $\infty^2$ points of a plane. An $R_2$ in $R_3$ is also represented by a linear equation. If we now add a second equation: $a_1x + b_1y + c_1z + d_1 = 0$, then the two equations together define a line, which is an $R_1$. An $R_1$ in an $R_3$ is therefore determined by two linear equations. We clearly see here that the linear spaces of different extension (dimensions) are defined by the number of linear equations in the coordinates $x$, $y$, $z$. Finally an $R_0$ is determined by three such equations; we say that three $R_2$ intersect in an $R_0$, and two $R_2$ intersect in an $R_1$.

If we have three linear equations $ax + \ldots = 0$, $a_1x + \ldots = 0$, $a_2x + \ldots = 0$, then, for example, we can consider the first two equations together, then the third alone and finally all three together. In this manner spaces $R_1$, $R_2$ and $R_0$ result. $R_1$ and $R_2$ have a certain $R_0$ in common; we thus recognize purely analytically that an $R_1$ intersects an $R_2$ in an $R_0$. From a geometrical point of view, this theorem may be expressed thus: A line cuts a plane in one point. This simple example suffices to show that theorems involving points, lines and planes are nothing else but relationships between equations of three variables which we express advantageously in geometrical language. We are now able to derive all the theorems of $R_0$, $R_1$, and $R_2$, which are defined by a definite number of equations and obtain an abstract geometry in $R_3$. We do not want to carry this out here, because these theorems correspond to statements concerning points, lines and planes in space, the knowledge of which we want to take for granted.

From observation it is easily deducted that $\infty^2$ lines and $\infty^2$ planes go through one point; we need only to convert the point to all the points of a plane by means of lines, and to lay planes through the point and through all lines in an arbitrary plane. Through a line pass $\infty^1$ planes. Even from the equation of a plane, which contains three essential constants, we recognize that in space there are $\infty^3$ planes. Somewhat more difficult to answer is the question concerning all lines in space. If a line is represented by two linear equations, then we can always calculate two variables from the third; for instance, $x = \alpha z + \beta$, $y = \gamma z + \delta$. There are, therefore, as many lines as arbitrary values that the constants, $\alpha$, $\beta$, $\gamma$, $\delta$ can assume. This number is therefore $\infty \cdot \infty \cdot \infty \cdot \infty = \infty^4$ for lines in space. The number of all the lines which intersect a fixed line is $\infty^3$, since there are $\infty^1$ points on the line and through each point pass $\infty^2$ lines, thus $\infty^1 \cdot \infty^2 = \infty^3$. In general we can state that if any system with a prescribed characteristic is determined by $k$ mutually independent numbers (parameters), then we can denote by $\infty^k$ the number of possible positions of this system.

How many lines do two or three fixed skew lines intersect? ($\infty^2$ respectively $\infty^1$.)

The abstract geometry of $R_3$ finds its geometrical treatment in stereometry and we can construct models for all theorems, models in which the points, lines and planes are represented by small spheres, thin cords or plates. This procedure is, nevertheless, not only very unwieldy and difficult, but it is also most tedious to develop such constructions. For this reason, it is sought to represent a system in space by a two-dimensional construction on the drawing board, where we can work easily with compass and ruler. This can be done easily by imagining every point $P$ in space vertically projected on the $[xy]$ and $[yz]$ planes of the coordinate system whereby we obtain points $P'(xy0)$ and $P''(0yz)$ (Figure 3). Then we place both these planes containing the points $P'$ and $P''$ together on the drawing surface in such a way that they have the same y-coordinate.

In this manner all points $P$ in space are associated with the image points (projections) $P'$, $P''$ (Figure 4); $P'$ and $P''$ are then, in this well-known representation, the horizontal and vertical projections of $P$; $y$ is the axis of the figure. Descriptive geometry teaches us to work with this type of projection, the rudiments of which we presume to be known. On the drawing surface there are then two superimposed coordinate systems, the $[xy]$ system for $P'$ and the $[yz]$ system for $P''$, whereby the coordinate $y$ is common to both image points. While it is not customary to use the coordinate systems in the horizontal and vertical projection procedure, we attach a special value to it, because it makes it possible for us to read off the coordinates $x$,

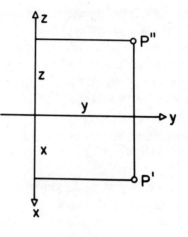

FIGURE 4

$y$, $z$ of every point in space directly from the projections on the drawing.

A surface $\epsilon$ can be represented in the familiar way by its traces $e_1$, $e_2$ (Figure 5). If the equation for the surface is

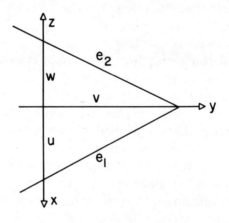

FIGURE 5

$ax + by + cz + d = 0$ and if $u$, $v$, $w$ are the interceptors of the axes, then the traces can be easily drawn in by means of the lines $u = -d/a$, $v = -d/b$, $w = -d/c$. If three linear equations in $x$, $y$, $z$ are given, then we can represent their respective planes by their traces; if we now seek the point of intersection of the three planes by descriptive geometry and read its coordinates, then we have solved the equation graphically.

# 4. POSITION RELATIONSHIPS

# AND MEASUREMENT

If one deals with space geometry, that is, if one investigates relationships between points, lines and planes, then one can distinguish between two kinds of theorems. If only operations of "connecting" and "intersecting" occur, then one has to do with relationships of position. If, in addition, concepts of length, area, volume, angle are involved, then one speaks of metrical theorems. Theorems having to do with the relationship of position are, for instance: two surfaces intersect in a line; through one point only one line can be drawn which intersects two given lines, etc. As we have already seen, the theorems of position denote, analytically, calculation with linear equations. Of the concepts of measurement, that of the length of a line is most important. If two given points $P_1(x_1 y_1 z_1)$ and $P_2(x_2 y_2 z_2)$ are given, the line $\overline{P_1 P_2}$ determined by them is represented by the expression:

$$\overline{P_1 P_2} = \left| \sqrt{(x_2 - x_1)^2 + (y_2 - y_1)^2 + (z_2 - z_1)^2} \right|.$$

All the remaining concepts of measurement can be derived from the concept of the length of a line or the distance between two points. Magnitudes of area and space can always be represented by lines. Angles, too, can be measured by lengths of lines, as is obvious from the trigonometric functions, which represent ratios of two lengths. This becomes clear from a geometric point of view, if we consider an angle formed by two intersecting lines as a triangle whose sides determine the angle. On the other hand, the angle formed by two planes, or the angle between a line and a plane, is reduced to an angle between two intersecting lines. Especially important metric concepts are the parallelism and the perpendicularity between two lines, two planes, and a line and a plane; this, of course, concerns the special angles of 0° and 90°. Examples of metric relationships are: only one line can be drawn perpendicular to two skew lines; from a single point to a surface only one perpendicular can be drawn—that is, there is only one line which can form a right angle with all lines drawn on the plane through its point of intersection, etc.

In the plane the distance between points $P_1(x_1 y_1)$ and $P_2(x_2 y_2)$ is expressed by an analogous equation, as in space (there is just one less coordinate):

$$\overline{P_1 P_2} = | \sqrt{(x_2 - x_1)^2 + (y_2 - y_1)^2} |.$$

In the same way the distance between two points $P_1(x_1)$ and $P_2(x_2)$ on a line is this single metrical relationship:

$$\overline{P_1 P_2} = | \sqrt{(x_2 - x_1)^2} | = | x_2 - x_1 |.$$

The distance equation thus possesses a fundamental significance in every geometry; we mean that by such an equation a determined "metric" is stamped on the space concerned, that is, a rule stated for the calculation of distances. This equation could have a different form but then the space would possess a different "metric." The given equations are basic for the so-called Euclidean geometry, the only geometry that concerns us here.

# 5. ABSTRACT $R_n$

We have considered the geometry of $R_1$, $R_2$, and $R_3$ in a manner that suggests an extrapolation into spaces of a higher order (higher dimensions). We have seen that the geometry in an $R_n(n = 1,2,3)$ is analytically nothing else but essentially the treatment of linear equations with $n$-variables, whereby the metric is defined by the pertinent distance equation. Now, if $n > 3$, i.e. if we deal with equations and systems of equations of more than three variables, we can proceed in the same manner, purely analytically, and say that we henceforth have a geometry of $R_n$ where $n > 3$. To be sure, this $R_n$ is purely an abstract concept for which, presently, we have no means of perception. According to our knowledge, a visual perception beyond the three-dimensional point space which represents the abstract $R_3$ is impossible; a geometrical representation of a higher $R_n$ is thus apparently out of the picture. But still we shall see that we can acquire, step by step, a geometric insight into higher space in several ways, and that the newly acquired concepts are no more difficult to comprehend, with proper practice, than our usual space concepts. We shall, of course, leave aside all "occultistic" fantasy and, always relying on clear mathematical precepts, we shall turn our attention immediately to very general considerations, which are nothing but a logical continuation of what has been presented this far.

If, in the mathematical treatment of any facts whatsoever,

we are concerned with $n$ variables $x_1, x_2, \ldots, x_i, \ldots, x_n$, which can take all possible real values, then we denote each possible group of these $n$ variables as "point" $P$ and say that $x_1, \ldots, x_n$ are its coordinates. The concept of "point" is therefore nothing more than an expression, borrowed from geometry, for a group of $n$ values, which, of course, must always be coordinated in a definite manner and where each $x_i$ always has the same significance; we also identify a point, to specify the values it represents, as $P(x_1, \ldots, x_n)$. From the earlier considerations it is clear that there are therefore a total of $\infty^n$ points, whose totality we express as an $n$-dimensional or $n$-times extended space and to which we attach the symbol $R_n$. This abstract $R_n$, with the visualization of which we do not want to concern ourselves at this stage, is therefore the field for all calculations with the $n$ variables. Since all calculations must be executed through equations, we are, in the first instance, led to the consideration of linear equations. Such an equation as

$$a_0 + a_1 x_1 + a_2 x_2 + a_3 x_3 + \ldots + a_{n-1} x_{n-1} + a_n x_n = 0$$

separates from the $R_n$ all points (value groups) which must satisfy it. Because all $n$ coordinates can now no longer be taken arbitrarily, but e.g. only the variables $x_1$ to $x_{n-1}$, where $x_n$ is already determined by the equation, there are now $\infty^{n-1}$ points which are given by the equation.

Their totality can be designated as linear $R_{n-1}$, for which the equation is just an equation in the $n$ coordinates. Nothing is changed herein if not all the $n$ coordinates appear in the equation; those that do not appear can be considered as free to be chosen at will.

If we take two linear equations, then all points which simultaneously satisfy both equations belong to an $R_{n-2}$; in general $k$ linear equations determine an $R_{n-k}$, or otherwise expressed: an $R_l$ is determined by $n - l$ linear equations. In particular, an $R_3$ possesses $n - 3$ equations, $R_2$ possesses $n - 2$, an $R_1$ possesses $n - 1$ and an $R_0$ possesses $n$ equations. In the last case, the $n$ equations produce directly a single group of values $x_1, \ldots, x_n$, thus a point for which the symbol $R_0$ is a necessary consequence. In this way are defined all the linear spaces within $R_n$, whose order of dimension (extension) must be smaller than $n$.

If an $R_l$ is represented by $n - l$ equations in $x_1, \ldots, x_n$, then $n - l$ coordinates may be expressed linearly by the remaining $l$ as follows:

$$\left. \begin{aligned}
x_{l+1} &= \alpha_{l+1}x_1 + \beta_{l+1}x_2 + \ldots + \lambda_{l+1}x + \mu_{l+1} \\
x_{l+2} &= \alpha_{l+2}x_2 + \beta_{l+2}x_2 + \ldots + \lambda_{l+2}x + \mu_{l+1} \\
&\cdot \quad \cdot \quad \cdot \quad \cdot \quad \cdot \quad \cdot \quad \cdot \quad \cdot \quad \cdot \quad \cdot \\
x_{n-1} &= \alpha_{n-1}x_1 + \beta_{n-1}x_2 + \ldots + \lambda_{n-1}x + \mu_{n-1} \\
x_n &= \alpha_n x_1 \; + \beta_n x_2 \;\; + \ldots + \lambda_n x \;\; + \mu_n
\end{aligned} \right\} \begin{aligned} &n - l \\ &\text{Equations.} \end{aligned}$$

This system comprises $(n - l)(l + 1)$ coefficients which are essential for $R_l$; from this presentation we can clearly observe that $x_1$ to $x_l$ can be chosen arbitrarily, but that the remaining coordinates of the points from $R$ are dependent upon them. The space $R_l$ is uniquely defined by the constants $\alpha, \beta, \ldots, \lambda, \mu$ since when these are known, we can immediately write down the equations for $R_l$. The question now arises as to how many points are needed to define a space $R_l$, i.e., how many points must be assumed to fix a single $R_l$, which among its $\infty^l$ points also contains the given points. This is the same as determining the necessary number of equations for the coefficients $\alpha, \beta, \ldots,$ $\lambda, \mu$. Since by the introduction of the coordinates of a single fixed point $(n - l)$ equations develop for the $(n - l)(l + 1)$ coefficients, one has to insert one by one into the equations the coordinates of $(l + 1)$ points, to obtain the necessary $(n - l)(l + 1)$ equations. We say: an $R_l$ is determined by $l + 1$ points, or only one $R_l$ can be drawn through $l + 1$ points. An $R_1$ is determined by 2 points of $R_n$, an $R_2$ by 3 points, etc. and an $R_{n-1}$ by $n$ points of $R_n$. To be sure, we must add that the points taken are in general positions, which means that no linear relationships may exist between their coordinates. We cannot continue further along this line at the present time. However, it is obvious that we are dealing essentially with the theory of linear equations with $n$ variables, whose relationships are expressed in geometrical language.

When all the coefficients in the $(n - l)$ equations of $R$ become zero, then we get a special $R_l$ with the equations:

$$x_{l+1} = 0, \ x_{l+2} = 0, \ \ldots, \ x_{n-1} = 0, \ x_n = 0.$$

The remaining variables $x_1$ to $x_l$ are now subject to no restrictions. The calculations within this $R_l$ are carried out in $x_1, \ldots, x_l$ just the same as if one had to deal from the beginning with only $l$ variables. In this way, one has a simple method to deal with geometry in a space of lower dimensional order than $R_n$. It is evident also that the geometry of $R_n$ embraces all geometries of space of lower order. For example, if we set

$$x_4 = 0, \ x_5 = 0, \ \ldots, \ x_n = 0,$$

then we get an $R_3$ in which only the coordinates, $x_1, x_2, x_3$ play a role; the same way, we can arrive at an $R_2$ possessing only the coordinates $x_1, x_2,$ and finally at an $R_1$ with the single coordinate $x_1$. If, for example, we are dealing with such an $R_3$, then we can consider the three coordinates of an abstract point $P(x_1 x_2 x_3)$ as the space coordinates of an actual point, and check geometrically all calculations with $x_1 x_2 x_3$. This is why one calls $R_3$ simply "space," if there is no danger of mistake. An equation $ax_1 + bx_2 + cx_3 + d = 0$, joining the equation $x_4 = x_5 = \ldots = x_n = 0$, gives an $R_2$ which in the "solid" space $R_3$ is represented by a surface. For this reason, one calls each $R_2$ a "plane" and furthermore, each $R_1$ a "line." An $R_{n-1}$ in $R_n$ will be called a hyperspace.

If we have an $R_k$ and an $R_l$ in an $R_n$, then both these spaces can have points in common—that is, groups of values, $x_1, \ldots, x_n$ can exist that satisfy the $n - k$ equations of $R_k$ and also the $n - l$ equations of $R_l$. Altogether we have then $2n - (k + l)$ equations in $x_1$ to $x_n$. These, however, can be generally satisfied only if the number of equations is $n$ at the most. If this is the case, then the $2n - (k + l)$ equations represent $R_{n-2n+(k+l)}$ or $R_{k+l-n}$ which we designate as an intersection of $R_k$ and $R_l$. We state the theorem thus obtained: an $R_k$ and $R_l$ intersect in an $R_{k+l-n}$, in case $k + l \geqq n$. In particular two $R_{n-1}$ intersect in an $R_{n-2}$. An $R_l$ and an $R_{n-l}$ have in general (at least) one $R_0$ in common. But if the sum of the dimensions for the given spaces $R_k$ and $R_l$ is $k + l < n$, then more than $n$ equations are present which, in general can be satisfied by no group of values $x_1, \ldots,$ $x_n$. One says that $R_k$ and $R_l$ do not intersect in case $k + l < n$. In theorems of this kind we must always add "in general" since $R_k$ and $R_l$ could be originally assumed to have a common space; but then $R_k$ and $R_l$ would not be completely independent of each other. It is obvious that we simply cannot know a priori whether two spaces intersect or not, but that we must know, in addition, in what space of higher dimension they are "lodged," i.e. coexist simultaneously. Therefore, two $R_1$ intersect only in an $R_2$, but generally no longer in an $R_3$. Two $R_2$ intersect in an $R_3$ forming an $R_1$, in an $R_4$ forming an $R_0$; but no longer in an $R_5$.

If, for example, two spaces $R_k$ and $R_l$ do not intersect, then one can always determine a space of minimum dimensions which just contains the $R_k$ and $R_l$. We can consider the $R_k$ as defined by $k + 1$ and the $R_l$ by $l + 1$ mutually independent points. This adds up to $k + l + 2$ points, through which a single $R_{k+l+1}$ passes; this we call their junction space. The junction space of an $R_k$ and an $R_0$, which does not lie in $R_k$, is thus an $R_{k+1}$. Thence, a plane is determined by a line and a point not on the line, an ordinary space by a plane and a point, and an $R_4$ by an $R_3$ and a point outside, which we could really determine if another point outside our space were known to us. Although perception of this by means of our senses is not possible, by abstract considerations we can reach $R_4$ and, step by step, even higher spaces.

From all this we understand how we can develop multi-dimensional geometry, although this would require the use of an extensive theory of the systems of linear equations which we shall not be able to expand on here. In the following, we want to consider in detail only the relationships in $R_4$. There exists, of course, a "metric" also in $R_4$; one can speak of distances, angles, parallel and perpendicular positions, and one can also presume that the more complicated these things become, the higher the $R_n$ under consideration. Each Euclidean metric in an $R_n$ can again be based on the distance equation; if $P(x_1, \ldots, x_n)$ and $P'(x_1', \ldots, x_n')$ are two points, then the distance between them is defined by

$$\overline{PP'} = \left| \sqrt{(x_1 - x_1')^2 + (x_2 - x_2')^2 + \ldots + (x_n - x_n')^2} \right|.$$

Finally, we want to adduce here, even if without proof, one more theorem: If $k + 1$ points of a space $R_k$ are found in a higher space $R_l$, then the entire $R_k$ lies in $R_l$. Applied particularly to an $R_1$, this means that if a line has two points in common with a space then it lies wholly within the space; or: the line connecting two points of a particular space lies wholly within this space. Therefore, the name "linear space" for an $R_l$ is geometrically justified.

> The reader should think about this theorem and about all the considerations contained in this section concerning the $R_3$ space, ($n = 3$), and compare this with his geometrical experience.

# 6. ABSTRACT $R_4$

From now on we shall concentrate on $R_4$ and designate as points, lines, planes and spaces the linear structures $R_0$, $R_1$, $R_2$,

$R_3$ contained therein. We shall also choose $x$, $y$, $z$, $t$ in this order for the coordinates of a point of $R_4$.

The following linear equations define the juxtaposed structures (viz: space, plane, line, point):

$$
\left.
\begin{array}{l}
ax + by + cz + dt + e = 0 \ : \text{space} \\
a_1x + b_1y + c_1z + d_1t + e_1 = 0 \quad \ldots \ . \\
a_2x + b_2y + c_2z + d_2t + e_2 = 0 \quad \ldots \ldots \ldots \\
a_3x + b_3y + c_3z + d_3t + e_3 = 0 \quad \ldots \ldots \ldots \ . \ .
\end{array}
\right\} \text{plane} \left. \vphantom{\begin{array}{l}a\\a\\a\end{array}} \right\} \text{line} \left. \vphantom{\begin{array}{l}a\\a\\a\\a\end{array}} \right\} \text{point.} \ (1)
$$

We always denote points with italic capital letters, $A$, $B$, $C$, $P$, ..., lines with lower case italic letters, $g$, $h$, $l$, ..., planes with lower case Greek letters, $\alpha$, $\beta$, $\gamma$, $\epsilon$, ..., spaces with Greek capitals, $\Delta$, $\Lambda$, $\Gamma$, .... For planes and lines we still write the explicit description:

$$
\left.
\begin{array}{l}
z = p_1x + q_1y + r_1 \\
t = p_2x + q_2y + r_2
\end{array}
\right\} R_2 \tag{2}
$$

$$
\left.
\begin{array}{l}
y = m_1x + n_1 \\
z = m_2x + n_2 \\
t = m_3x + n_3
\end{array}
\right\} R_1 \tag{3}
$$

There are thus $\infty^4$ points, $\infty^6$ lines, $\infty^6$ planes and $\infty^4$ spaces in $R_4$. A line is determined by two points, a plane by three, and a space by four points in general position (with mutually independent linear coordinates). Thus, for example, we cannot say that three points are generally situated if they lie on a line; for then the insertion of their coordinates into the equations (3) would furnish twelve values which would have to satisfy nine equations. That is, the eight coordinates of two points can be freely chosen but only one more can be taken from the third point. Likewise, four points are not independent of each other, when they lie on a plane or on a line. Finally five points in a general position cannot lie in one space, on one plane or on one line.

If we apply the considerations of $R_n$ to $R_4$, then without more ado we obtain the intersection theorems, summarized in the table below where, at the cross-point of the rows and columns, the intersection space of the pertinent structures is recorded:

|       | Space | Plane | Line  |
|-------|-------|-------|-------|
| Space | Plane | Line  | Point |
| Plane | Line  | Point |       |
| Line  | Point |       |       |

The blank spaces signify that in general no intersection exists. Three spaces have one line in common and four spaces have a point in common, as can be read directly from the equations (1).

The laws governing the inter-penetration of spaces may now be expressed thus: a line lies on a plane or in a space if two of its points lie in it; a plane lies in a space when three of its points lie in it. For example, we want to demonstrate the theorem concerning line and space—the reader may himself try to prove the other two theorems. Let a space be defined by the first equation from (1), and a line by (3). If now $P_1(x_1 y_1 z_1 t_1)$ and $P_2(x_2 y_2 z_2 t_2)$ are two points on the line as well as in the space, then the four equations are joined by the following additional ones:

$$y_1 = m_1 x_1 + n_1 \qquad\qquad y_2 = m_1 x_2 + n_1$$
$$z_1 = m_2 x_1 + n_2 \qquad\qquad z_2 = m_2 x_2 + n_2$$
$$t_1 = m_3 x_1 + n_3 \qquad\qquad t_2 = m_3 x_2 + n_3$$

$$ax_1 + by_1 + cz_1 + dt_1 + e = 0$$
$$ax_2 + by_2 + cz_2 + dt_2 + e = 0.$$

From the equations of the lines we can derive

$$y - y_1 = m_1(x - x_1) \text{ and } y_2 - y_1 = m_1(x_2 - x_1);$$

from which:

$$\frac{y - y_1}{y_2 - y_1} = \frac{x - x_1}{x_2 - x_1}$$

and similarly

$$\frac{z - z_1}{z_2 - z_1} = \frac{x - x_1}{x_2 - x_1} \quad \text{and} \quad \frac{t - t_1}{t_2 - t_1} = \frac{x - x_1}{x_2 - x_1}.$$

Now we set the value of the fraction $(x - x_1)/(x_2 - x_1) = \mu$, where $\mu$ is a variable parameter dependent on $x$; or vice versa, $x$ is determined when $\mu$ is assumed. Summarizing, one can write:

$$\frac{x - x_1}{x_2 - x_1} = \frac{y - y_1}{y_2 - y_1} = \frac{z - z_1}{z_2 - z_1} = \frac{t - t_1}{t_2 - t_1} = \mu.$$

From this we obtain:

$$\left.\begin{aligned}
x &= (1 - \mu)x_1 + \mu x_2 \\
y &= (1 - \mu)y_1 + \mu y_2 \\
z &= (1 - \mu)z_1 + \mu z_2 \\
t &= (1 - \mu)t_1 + \mu t_2
\end{aligned}\right\} \tag{4}$$

Thus, an arbitrary point $P(xyzt)$ of the line connecting points $P_1$ and $P_2$, is defined by means of a variable parameter; that is, by the choice of a value for $\mu$ we obtain at once all four coordinates of a running point $P$. We designate therefore the equations (4) as the parameter equations of a line drawn through two points. The coordinates of $P$, inserted in the space equation, must satisfy these identically:

$$a[(1 - \mu)x_1 + \mu x_2] + b[(1 - \mu)y_1 + \mu y_2] +$$
$$+ c[(1 - \mu)z_1 + \mu z_2] + d[(1 - \mu)t_1 + \mu t_2] + e = 0$$

$$(1 - \mu)[ax_1 + by_1 + cz_1 + dt_1] +$$
$$+ \mu[ax_2 + by_2 + cz_2 + dt_2] + e = 0.$$

The expressions in the square brackets yield, however, from the stipulation that $P_1$ and $P_2$ lie in the space, the value $-e$; hence we finally arrive at the identity equation:

$$(1 - \mu)(-e) + \mu(-e) + e \equiv 0.$$

Since a straight line which connects two points of a plane or a space belongs entirely to the respective space system, it is possible, if two points are required to define a system, to replace these two points by the line passing through them or by any other two points on this same line. In the same manner, three points can represent the plane drawn through them.

We can make use of this fact, e.g., if a space is defined by four points $A$, $B$, $C$, $D$, if we arrange the points into groups. If we consider $A$ alone and $B$, $C$, $D$ together, then the space is determined by a point and a plane. If we take the groups $A$, $B$, and $C$, $D$, then we recognize that a space can also be represented by two lines. We are thus here concerned with special theorems on the connecting spaces.

Now, if we have a given space and a point $P$ lying without, then we can connect $P$ with all the $\infty^3$ points of the space. Each of such connecting lines has all points—with exception of only one—outside the space; for, if there were a second point in the space, then the line would lie entirely within and could not contain $P$, which we have assumed to lie outside the space. The $\infty^3$ lines which go through $P$ completely fulfill $R_4$, for on each line there are $\infty^1$ points, in all thus $\infty^1 \cdot \infty^3 = \infty^4$ points, all different from each other (with the exception of $P$) and thus must form an $R_4$. One can state, in fact, that $R_4$ can be engendered from $R_3$ and an outside-lying point. The generation of a space from a plane and a point not lying on it takes place in the same way, which we of course also know from inspection. Through one point pass $\infty^3$ spaces, since the equation for such a point has four essential constants which are subject to one restriction. Through a line pass as many spaces as pass simultaneously through two points, thus $\infty^2$. Through a plane pass $\infty^1$ spaces.

Through a point pass $\infty^4$ planes, since the six coefficients of (2) are subjected to two restrictions, by the selection of a point. Further, $\infty^2$ planes pass through a line (or two points) because of the appearance of four equations of condition. Through one point pass $\infty^3$ lines, as has already been shown.

All foregoing theorems regarding $R_4$ belong to the geometry of position since they are concerned only with connections and intersections of the systems. We want to demonstrate one more such theorem which is typical for the geometry of position. We ask for all lines which simultaneously intersect three lines $g_1, g_2, g_3$. Through $g_1$ and $g_2$ a space $\Delta$ can be located which is cut by $g_3$ at point $P$. Now since $g_1, g_2$ and $P$ lie in space $\Delta$, only one line $g$ can be located through $P$ which touches $g_1$ and $g_2$. Hence, there exists only a single line which intersects three lines of $R_4$. But we must be strongly reminded that this geometrically expressed theorem, for which we do not as yet have a visual representation, actually expresses only its analytical content. If we remember that each of four lines $g_1, g_2, g_3, g$ represents three linear equations in four variables, then this theorem reads: For three groups of three equations each, there is but one group of three new equations of a type that the new group has only one solution in common with each of the three given groups. It is essential here that all equations have four variables.

# 7. MEASUREMENT IN ABSTRACT $R_4$

The "distance" of two points $P_1(x_1y_1z_1t_1)$ and $P_2(x_2y_2z_2t_2)$ is defined, as before, by the formula

$$\overline{P_1P_2} = |\sqrt{(x_1 - x_2)^2 + (y_1 - y_2)^2 + (z_1 - z_2)^2 + (t_1 - t_2)^2}|. \quad (5)$$

If we take a point $P_3(x_3 y_3 z_3 t_3)$ in addition to this, then we can connect $P_1$ with $P_2$ and $P_1$ with $P_3$, by one line each. As with the angle formed by the two lines intersecting in $P_1$, we want to consider that formed at $P_1$ by the triangle $P_1 P_2 P_3$ which can be calculated or constructed from the distances $\overline{P_1P_2}$, $\overline{P_2P_3}$, $\overline{P_3P_1}$. If, especially, the angle of 2 lines drawn through $P_1$ should be a right angle, then the relationship

$$\overline{P_1P_2}^2 + \overline{P_1P_3}^2 = \overline{P_2P_3}^2$$

must hold, where $P_2$ and $P_3$ are arbitrary points on both lines.

It is obvious that we can also speak of angles formed by interaction of the other system or elements, especially of the perpendicularity of two such elements; but we will deal with some of these things later on.

There are, however, some things that we want to say about parallelism. We consider two lines as parallel when they lie in the same plane and have no point of intersection; or we could say that their point of intersection is infinitely distant. A line is parallel to a plane when both lie in a space and when their point of intersection is at infinity. A line is parallel to a space when their point of intersection is infinitely distant. Analytically, such an infinitely distant point is indicated when at least one of its coordinates becomes $\infty$; in general this will, however, be the case with all coordinates.

Because a plane always intersects a space in a line, one can consider plane and space as parallel if the line of intersection cannot be found in the finite space, i.e., if the intersection is at an infinite distance. Two spaces are then parallel when their plane of intersection is infinitely distant—that is, if they have no single point in common in finite space.

Two planes can intersect in a point or in a line: in the first case they are in a "general" position; in the second case, they partake of the same space. If this point of intersection moves to infinity, then we say that both planes are half parallel. If they lie in a space and if the line of intersection lies at infinity, then we say they are completely parallel.

# 8. REPRESENTATION OF $R_4$

Now we want to express the structures of four-dimensional space by means of figures on the drawing board, which allow representation and evaluation of the different positions and measurement relationships by graphical methods. We have already done something similar with $R_3$, in which we have represented each of its points by their horizontal and vertical projections (plan and elevation views), thus by two points on the drawing surface. We imagine that we have two right angular coordinate systems $[xy]$ and $[zt]$ arranged in the drawing plane as shown in Figure 6; here, the positive axes' directions are indicated by arrows. This assumption is, thus, a simple extension of Figure 4 about the $t$-axis. There appear now also a $[yz]$ and a $[tx]$ system. Now, if a point $P$ of the abstract $R_4$ has the coordinates $x, y, z, t$, then we relate the first two coordinates to the $[xy]$ system, by which a point $P'$ is determined, and the remaining two to the $[zt]$ system, from which a point $P''$ results.

The point $P(x, y, z, t)$ is thus represented by the points $P'(x, y)$ and $P''(z, t)$ on the drawing surface. We call $P'$ the first representation and $P''$ the second representation of $P$. These two representations are completely independent of each other, and if we accept this we can immediately read the 4

coordinates of the corresponding point of $R_4$. In the [$yz$] system
we can determine, further, a point $\overline{P}$ whose coordinates agree
with the $y$ and $z$ of $P$. $\overline{P}$ is called the auxiliary view of $P$; it can
be constructed from $P'$ and $P''$, as can be seen in Figure 6. The
line in the plane of the drawing which represents both the $x$ and
$z$ axes we shall call $X$, and the other $Y$. The parallels to these
lines are called the $X$-director and $Y$-director. Accordingly, we
obtain the auxiliary view, in which we cause the $X$-director and
the first view, and the $Y$-director and the second view, to intersect.

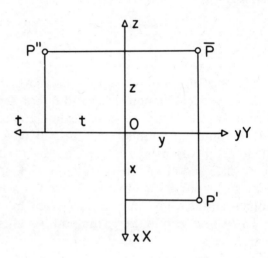

FIGURE 6

Figure 6 shows a point $P$ whose coordinates are all positive.
The reader should consider all possible positions of the views,
even if negative coordinates appear.

The point with the coordinates 0, 0, 0, 0, is called the
origin, both its views fall on the point of intersection $O$ of $X$
and $Y$.

# 9. COORDINATE SPACES

# AND PERPENDICULARITY

Because a space is determined by one linear equation, a plane by two and a line by three linear equations, the equations $y = 0$, $z = 0$, $t = 0$ ($x$ is arbitrary) give a line which we call the $x$ axis of $R_4$. If a point $P$ lies on $[x]$, $P'$ must lie on X, and $P''$ on O, on the drawing surface. Similarly there are also the axes $[y]$, $[z]$, $[t]$. The reader should consider the representation of points on these axes. The four axes pass through the origin. If we take, for example, $P$ on $[x]$, $Q$ on $[z]$ and consider the triangle $O(0, 0, 0, 0)$, $P(x, 0, 0, 0)$, $Q(0, 0, z, 0)$, then according to the distance formula $\overline{OP} = x$, $\overline{OQ} = z$, $\overline{PQ} = \sqrt{x^2 + z^2}$, and then $\overline{OP^2} + \overline{OQ^2} = \overline{PQ^2}$.

Therefore these two axes are perpendicular to each other and so are any other two axes. The four coordinate axes enclose, in pairs, six right angles.

The equations $z = 0$, $t = 0$, produce a plane, the so-called coordinate plane $[xy]$, in which the points have arbitrary coordinates $[x]$ and $[y]$. The first views of such points are arbitrary; the second views fall according to the origin. The axes $[x]$ and $[y]$ lie in $[xy]$. We thus obtain a coordinate plane when we place the plane through two arbitrary axes. Similarly one has the planes $[xz]$, $[xt]$, $[yz]$, $[zt]$; the views of the points lying thereon are easily handled. We denote, in general, a line as normal to a plane when it forms a right angle with two lines of the plane. Because $[z]$ is normal to $[x]$ as well as to $[y]$, it is also normal to the plane $[xy]$. In general we find that each coordinate plane is normal to each axis which does not lie on the plane. If $P(x, y, 0, 0)$ is a point on $[xy]$ and $Q(0, 0, 0, t)$ a point on $[t]$, then the relationship $\overline{OP}^2 + \overline{OQ}^2 = \overline{PQ}^2$ again holds. $[t]$ thus forms a right angle with each line drawn through $O$ on $[xy]$. This theorem has also general validity for lines which are normal to a plane, if they intersect in a point—that is, if they lie in one space. Since $[z]$ as well as $[t]$ are normal to $[xy]$, we say that the planes $[xy]$ and $[zt]$ and generally two arbitrary co-ordinate planes are perpendicular to each other. In general, then, we would interpret two planes as normal to each other when one of them passes through two normals which can be constructed at a point on the other plane. From the preceding theorem it follows directly that when two planes are perpendicular to each other, two arbitrary lines passing through the point of intersection of the planes, and lying in different planes, form right angles. At one point on a plane we can construct an infinite number of normals to $R_4$ which satisfy* the normal plane. This derives from the fact that we can place $\infty^1$ spaces through a plane and in each of these spaces we can place one single normal at one point on the plane. If two planes intersect in one line, then they belong to one space and must obey the known rules of solid geometry regarding perpendicularity.

The equation $t = 0$ defines a coordinate space $[xyz]$, which passes through the three axes $[x]$, $[y]$, $[z]$ and also contains the planes $[xy]$, $[xz]$, $[yz]$. The views of the points from $[xyz]$ are subject to the limitation $t = 0$ that is, the second views must lie on $X$.The same holds for the remaining spaces $[xyt]$, $[xzt]$, and $[yzt]$. The axis $[t]$ is normal to $[x]$, $[y]$, and $[z]$ and is therefore designated as normal to the space $[xyz]$. In general, we say a line is normal to a space when it is perpendicular to three lines lying in the space which pass through their point of intersection. It is easy to show that $[t]$ then is normal to every line lying in $[xyz]$ and passing through $O$. One designates a plane as being perpendicular to a space when it passes through a normal; in

* Can also be read "fill."

the same way, a space passing through the normal of another space is normal to the original. Therefore each coordinate space forms a right angle with each coordinate plane not lying in it, just as do arbitrary coordinate spaces with respect to each other.

# 10. THE PROJECTION OF POINTS IN SPACE
## ONTO THE COORDINATE PLANES

If we have a point $P(x, y, z, t)$ of $R_4$ and an arbitrary plane $\epsilon$, we can connect an arbitrary point $P_1$ on this plane with $P$ by a line. The shortest of these connecting lines $\overline{PP_1}$ we denote as the distance of point $P$ from $\epsilon$. We call point $P_1$ the projection of $P$ on $\epsilon$. We will take the coordinate plane $[xy]$ as $\epsilon$, where $P_1$ shall have the coordinates $x_1, y_1, 0, 0$. The distance $\overline{PP_1}$ is then

$$\overline{PP_1} = \sqrt{(x-x_1)^2 + (y-y_1)^2 + z^2 + t^2}.$$

If we want this expression to become a minimum at fixed $x, y, z, t$ then $x_1$ must be equal to $x$ and $y_1$ to $y$. The projection from $O(x, y, z, t)$ on $[xy]$ is thus point $P_1(x, y, 0, 0)$. Similarly we obtain the projection of $P$ on the other coordinate surfaces by setting, in each case, two coordinates to zero. $P_2(0, y, z, 0)$ is the projection on $[yz]$ and $P_3(0, 0, z, t)$ is the projection on $[zt]$. Now we can also show that $\overline{PP_1}$ is normal to $[xy]$. If $Q(\xi, \eta, 0, 0)$ is an arbitrary point of $[xy]$, then

$$\overline{PP_1} = \sqrt{x^2 + t^2}, \quad \overline{P_1Q} = \sqrt{(x-\xi)^2 + (y-\eta)^2}$$

and
$$\overline{PQ} = \sqrt{(x - \xi)^2 + (y - \eta)^2 + z^2 + t^2},$$

therefore
$$\overline{PP_1}^2 + \overline{P_1Q}^2 = \overline{PQ}^2$$

thus there is always a right angle at $P_1$ in the triangle $PP_1Q$. Accordingly we can obtain the projection of a point on a plane also by imagining that the point and the plane are connected by means of a space which has its normal constructed in the usual way. In Figure 7 we draw the three views of $P$ and its three projections $P_1$, $P_2$, $P_3$ on the coordinate planes. We see that $P'_1$ coincides with $P'$, $\overline{P}_2$ with $\overline{P}$, and $P''_3$ with $P''$. We can thus conceive the three views of $P$ as being established as follows: we project $P$ successively onto the coordinate planes $[xy]$, $[yz]$, $[zt]$ and bring these two planes together with the projections $P_1$, $P_2$, $P_3$ lying therein in such a manner on the drawing surface

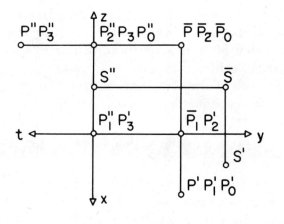

FIGURE 7

that the planes remain coherent on the coordinate axes. Then points $P_1$, $P_2$, $P_3$ give the respective image points $P'$, $\overline{P}$, $P''$. We can achieve the same thing also in the following manner: we will first imagine the $[zt]$ plane rotated around the $[z]$ axis into the [$yz$] plane, which we can easily imagine since both planes lie in one space. Continuing, we revolve the two planes, thus joined, around the [$y$] axis into the [$xy$] plane. Thus by double rotation around two lines we can bring together all three planes into one, which then can be made to coincide with the drawing surface.

# 11. RELATING $R_4$ TO THE DRAWING SURFACE.

# THE DESCRIPTIVE GEOMETRY OF $R_4$

Now by reversing the procedures depicted above, we can imagine the coordinate system of $R_4$ constructed on the drawing plane. On the drawing plane, we let the axes $x$ and $y$ be simultaneously the axes [$x$] and [$y$] of $R_4$, hence the drawing plane is the [$xy$] plane. At point $O$, we imagine the [$z$] axis normal to the drawing surface, having the drawing in the horizontal position, with the positive part of the line directed upwards. If we fold down the [$yz$] plane, which is normal to the drawing plane, then [$z$] comes into position $z$. By the three mutually normal and easily imagined axes [$x$], [$y$], [$z$], the space [$xyz$] is represented, which now is identical to the customary space of our senses. We will denote this $R_3$, which of course is our conceptual space, by the special label $\boldsymbol{R}_3$; its equation within $R_4$ is of course $t = 0$. Still missing is the fourth axis [$t$], whose position we can however no longer represent. Now we have to accept, by pure logic and on the basis of the previous results, that [$t$] is the normal, constructed on $\boldsymbol{R}_3$ at $O$. In a certain measure, we can visualize only those structures of $R_4$ that are in $R_3$. Therefore, we find ourselves in a position similar to that of a hypothetical being who has his habitat on a plane and now wants to take cognizance of $R_3$, in which the plane is found. Whether or not there is an $R_4$ in which our $R_3$ lies, we will never be able to determine because of the limitation of our senses. We must therefore think the more highly of the mental effort needed to construct this $R_4$ even if its actual existence can never be proven.

The views of a point $S$ of our $R_3$ are drawn in Figure 7, in which we must note that $S''$ must always lie on X. Then $S'$ and $S$ are, of course, according to our previous considerations, the plan and elevation views of $S$. We see how the method of the plan and elevation views of the customary $R_3$ reveals itself as a special case of representing $R_4$ by being simply its application to $R_3$ (compare Figure 4 to Figure 6). Therefore we can designate the procedure given in section 8, which we will use exclusively from now on as the descriptive geometry of $R_4$.

Even if we cannot form a visual concept of $R_4$, we can still connect its points to those of $R_3$, in a simple manner. The distance of the point $P(x, y, z, t)$ from a point $S(\xi, \eta, \zeta, 0)$ of $R_3$ is the same as

$$\overline{PS} = \sqrt{(x - \xi)^2 + (y - \eta)^2 + (z - \zeta)^2 + t^2}.$$

The shortest of all these connections appears, then, when the radicand reaches a minimum, which is the case with $\xi = x$, $\eta = y$, $\zeta = z$; the point $P_0(x, y, z, 0)$ so obtained we call the projection of $P$ on $R_3$. It is easily shown that $\overline{PP_0}^2 + \overline{P_0S}^2 = \overline{PS}^2$ and that accordingly $\overline{PP_0}$ is perpendicular to $R_3$; the length of this perpendicular is $t$. In Figure 7 the views of $P_0$ are also drawn. Obviously, the first view and auxiliary view of $P$ are the plan and elevation views of the projection of $P$ to $R_3$. We can, therefore, obtain point $P(x, y, z, t)$ in such a way that we first choose point $P_0(x, y, z, 0)$ in $R_3$, erect in it the perpendicular to $R_3$ and lay off on it the distance $t$. This mental construction corresponds to the addition of $P''$ to $P'$ and $\overline{P}$ in the graphic construction. The first view of this perpendicular is point $P' \equiv P_0'$; the second view of it is the line $\overline{P_0''P'}$.

## 12. LINES AND DISTANCES IN $R_4$

      The knowledge gained thus far of the descriptive geometry of $R_4$ we will want to use for the purpose of obtaining, by means of constructions on the drawing board, a clear insight into the structure of $R_4$ and in this way develop a type of concrete visualization of $R_4$. We shall occasionally leave out the axes X and Y (see Figure 6) when they are not absolutely necessary. We give two points $P_1(x_1y_1z_1t_1)$ and $P_2(x_2y_2z_2t_2)$ in their respective views (Figure 8) and want the views of the lines of connection $P_1P_2$, which will be called $g$. The coordinates of a movable point $P(xyzt)$ of $g$ are represented by the equations (4) by means of a parameter. The first two equations state, however, that $P'(xy)$ must lie on the connecting line $g'$ from $P_1'$ and $P_2'$; this also goes for the auxiliary view $\overline{g}$ and the second view $g''$. The three views of $g$, therefore, are again lines. If $P$ runs through the line $g$, so also do the three views (as we can see from the drawing) simultaneously run through similar series of points on the line views; i.e. there is always:

$$\overline{P'P_1'} : \overline{P'P_2'} = \overline{\overline{P}\overline{P}_1} : \overline{\overline{P}\overline{P}_2} = \overline{P''P_1''} : \overline{P''P_2''}.$$

To express a line, the views of two points suffice; so we can omit the auxiliary views. The auxiliary view is, however, very helpful for easy construction of the associated views of an arbitrary point of a line, by means of the monitor lines.

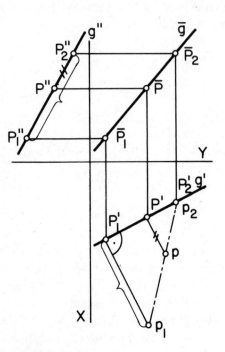

FIGURE 8

However, two lines $g'$ and $g''$ alone do not suffice for fixing the line g, because we have no anchor point for coordinating the views of the point; there we have to take also the auxiliary view $\bar{g}$ and then work with the monitors.

The reader should construct the intersections of line $g$ with the four coordinate spaces, especially with $\boldsymbol{R}_3(t = 0)$.

The length of the line $\overline{P_1P_2}$ is given by equation (5). But now the first view of the line of $\overline{P_1P_2}$ is given by $\sqrt{(x_1 - x_2)^2 + (y_1 - y_2)^2} = \overline{P_1'P_2'}$, and the second by $\sqrt{(z_1 - z_2)^2 + (t_1 - t_2)^2} = \overline{P_1''P_2''}$. Therefore

$$\overline{P_1P_2}^2 = \overline{P_1'P_2'}^2 + \overline{P_1''P_2''}^2.$$

We can, therefore, get the true length of a line of $R_4$ if we look for the hypotenuse of a right triangle where the legs are both lines of the views. This fundamental construction is given in Figure 8, where the first line of the view is used as one leg of the triangle. The distance $P_2P_1$ gives the length of $\overline{P_2P_1}$. If we likewise draw the associated triangle above $\overline{P_2'P'}$ then $P$ falls on the hypotenuse $P_2P_1$ and we obtain from this the true lengths according to which $P$ divides the line $\overline{P_2P_1}$. The lines of the views are hence in the same relationship as the lines in space. We can, therefore, use this construction to lay off a given length on a line, from a given point.

> Draw a line in $R_3$, determine its length and compare this construction to the known principle of plan and elevation views.

If, for example, we let the first views of two points $P_1$, $P_2$ coincide (Figure 9), then $g'$ becomes a point—i.e., all first views of the point on the line fall together—$g$ is parallel to X. The true length of the line is shown by $\overline{P_1''P_2''}$. From the next section we shall see that we can draw a parallel to $g$ through $O$, which lies in the $[zt]$ plane. But this parallel is normal to the $[xy]$ plane. Therefore, we consider $g$ as normal to $[xy]$, even though it does not cut this plane. An analogous situation exists in $R_3$ for two lines which cross, for which we also get an angle.

> Draw a normal to the $[zt]$ plane! What are the relationships when $\bar{g}$ becomes a point? Which lines are formed when two of their views are reduced to points? Consider the views of the axes! (Everything is associated with section 13).

If for an arbitrary line $g$ we take equations (3) as a basis for consideration, then the first equation will give the view $g'$,

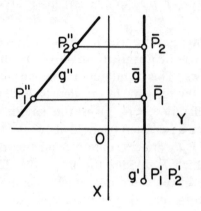

FIGURE 9

the two first equations give view $g$ after elimination of $x$, and the last two give view $g''$ after the elimination of $x$.

## 13. PARALLEL LINES

If we have a line $g$ (Figure 10) and, externally, a point $P$, then we can connect $P$ with an arbitrary point $Q$ of $g$; the lines $g$ and $PQ$ then intersect, and thus lie in a plane. If we allow $Q$ to extend farther and farther, then $PQ$ remains on this plane and becomes parallel to $g$ (designated in Figure 10 by $h$), in the extreme case if $Q$ goes to infinity. We see that corresponding views of parallel lines are again parallel, and it is easy to draw $h$ parallel to $g$ through $P$ if we work with all three views. If we

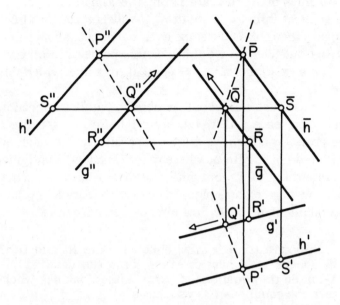

FIGURE 10

take two lines $\overline{QR}$ and $\overline{PS}$ on $g$ and $h$, then we obtain, because of the monitor:

$$\overline{P'S'} : \overline{Q'R'} = \overline{\bar{P}\bar{S}} : \overline{\bar{Q}\bar{R}} = \overline{P''S''} : \overline{Q''R''} = \overline{PS} : \overline{QR}.$$

This yields the theorem: parallel lines have, as views, also parallel lines which are in the same relationship as the lines in space. Particularly, the views of parallelograms in $R_4$ appear again as parallelograms.

If the view of a straight line is a point, then the corresponding views of the parallels must likewise be points.

What do the parallels to the coordinate axes look like? Draw through $P$ the parallel to $[t]$ and determine the intersection with $\boldsymbol{R}_3$.

All lines of $R_4$ that are parallel to a given line have the same point at infinity. If we draw parallels through all points of a space, then this is the same as if we connect all its points to one lying outside, but we think of this point as infinitely distant. There exist, therefore, $\infty^3$ parallels to a line, which fill the entire $R_4$.

One can also talk about an oblique parallel projection of $R_4$ on a fixed space $\Delta$. If we take a straight line $l$ as the direction of the projection, then we draw the parallel to $l$ through every point $P$ and cut it with $\Delta$, whereby the "shadow" $P^s$ originates. The same thing in $\boldsymbol{R}_3$, but with one dimension less, is the inclined view on a picture plane. The vertical parallel projection of the points of $R_4$ on $\boldsymbol{R}_3$ has already been discussed.

> Project a triangle ABC obliquely onto $\boldsymbol{R}_3$ and further, by means of a new direction, onto the drawing plane. What do the equations of parallel lines look like when we take the equations (3) as a basis?

# 14. THE REPRESENTATION OF THE PLANE

A plane $\epsilon$ is determined by three points $A$, $B$, $C$, which do not lie in a line (Figure 11). We can also define the plane by point $A$ and the line $BC$, or by the intersecting lines $AB$, $AC$. If we connect $A$ to a point $D$ on $BC$ by a line, then the construction must lie entirely in the plane. Now we can assume a point $P$ situated on $AD$, and in this manner we can obtain all points of $\epsilon$. The corresponding constructions in the three views can be made exactly the same as the constructions in customary de-

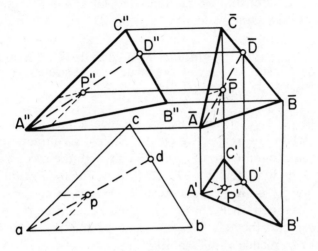

FIGURE 11

scriptive geometry in plan, elevation and auxiliary views. We can obtain a concept of the actual relationships if we imagine the plane $\epsilon$ removed from $R_4$ and placed on the picture plane. For this, it is only necessary to look for the length of the sides and to construct therewith the triangle *ABC*; with help from D we can also draw the correct position P inside the triangle. Now we can also execute on the drawing surface desired constructions in $\epsilon$ and project back the points found in the views; one always deals here with construction lines and their inversions. We can proceed even more simply in the case of several points, if we take AB and AC to be the axes of an oblique parallel coordinate system in $\epsilon$, and relate to it every point P. Then the coordinates can be read off on AB or AC or they can be retroverted. If we have once constructed *ABC*, then this procedure has the advantage that we now have only to do with lines on *AB* and *CD* and need only to construct parallelograms. For the relationship of the lines on ***AB*** and *A'B'* e.g., we always use the same scale.

Construct the altitudes of a triangle in an inscribed or circumscribed circle! Construct the distance of a point from a line.

In general, $\epsilon$ cuts each of the coordinate surfaces $[xy]$, $[yz]$, $[zt]$ in the respective points $E_1$, $E_2$, $E_3$ (tracer points). These are found from the conditions where the second view of $E_1$ and the first view of $E_3$ lie on $O$. It is true for $E_2$ that $E_2'$ lies on $Y$ and $E_2''$ on $X$. For this purpose, we have to consider $Y$ as a line $g'$ in the first view of the plane, and construct $g''$ from this; where $g''$ cuts the axis $X$, $E_2''$ is already found; from this we find $E_2'$ on $Y$ by means of the monitor lines.

The plane $\epsilon$ is defined by the tracer triangle $E_1E_2E_3$ as well as by any other triangle.

Carry out this construction when, in Figure 11, the axes have been added.

If we imagine all points from $\epsilon$ represented in the three views, then we get three fields of points $\epsilon'$ $\bar{\epsilon}$, and $\epsilon''$ on the drawing surface, which they cover entirely in each instance. Between each two such fields there exists a relationship of points such that parallel lines of one field correspond to those of the other. Parallel lines in all three fields are in the same relationship to each other. We call such a relationship between each two image fields an "affinity." A plane is thus represented on the drawing board by an affinity, i.e. by the affinity between $\epsilon'$ and $\epsilon''$, which in turn is fixed by the triangles $A'B'C'$ and $A''B''C''$. This affinity is represented analytically by the equations (2), which determine how point $P''(z, t)$ can be found from the first view of $P'$ $(x, y)$.

Taking the triangle *ABC*, we can let the first views $A'B'C'$

fall in a line (Figure 12). This will in no way change the construction of an arbitrary point $P$. But if $P'$ is given, we must
naturally know on which line $P$ lies, since otherwise we can
determine neither $P$ nor $P''$. If, for example, we let $P'$ coincide
with $C'$, and state that $P$ will lie on $AB$, then $\bar{P}$ and $P''$ are easily
found by means of the monitors. The line $PC$ is then a perpendicular to the plane $[xy]$. The first views of all parallels to $PC$
are points, and there is just one such line which goes through

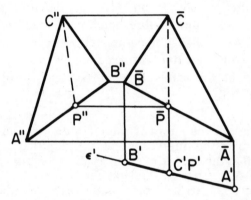

FIGURE 12

the first trace-point $E_1$, i.e. the point of intersection of $\epsilon$ with
$[xy]$. $\epsilon$ goes through a line which is normal to a point lying on
$[xy]$. We say that $\epsilon$ is half normal to $[xy]$ as opposed to a plane
which goes through two normals of $[xy]$ and only then is called
normal. For this reason, we designate the plane represented in
Figure 12 as "semi-first-projecting." Since all the first views of
the points from $\epsilon$ fall in the line $A'B'$, we can label this line $\epsilon'$,
it being the first view of $\epsilon$.

Represent a "semi-second-projecting" plane and determine its trace-triangle. What lines appear in the first view in true length?

It is also possible that all first views of point $\epsilon$ fall in a line $\epsilon'$ and all second views in a line $\epsilon''$. The equations of $\epsilon'$ and $\epsilon''$

$$px + qy + r = 0$$
$$\epsilon' : \epsilon'' : p_1z + q_1t + r_1 = 0$$

are, then, the equations of this special plane $\epsilon$. A point $P'$ on $\epsilon'$ and an arbitrary point $P''$ on $\epsilon''$ always denote a point $P$ of $\epsilon$. However, if, for example, three such points are taken, then the triangle thus established is completely defined as to its size, as is evident from the line construction. $\epsilon$ is now half-normal to $[xy]$ and at the same time to $[zt]$, and is called "double-projecting."

What do the views of the $[yz]$ and $[xt]$ plane look like? Determine the intersection of a generally positioned plane with $\boldsymbol{R_3}$ (the second view of the line of intersection must fall on X because $t = 0$). How can we find the point of intersection $S$ of an arbitrary plane with a double-projecting one, which is represented by $\epsilon'$ and $\epsilon''$? Notice that $S'$ must line on $\epsilon'$, and $S''$ on $\epsilon''$.

A special case of a plane $\epsilon$ represented by three points $ABC$ is also the one where $A'$, $B'$, $C'$ coincide in a single point, while $A''B''C''$ form a triangle. Then all the first views of the points of $\epsilon$ must fall according to $A'$, which is thus the first view $\epsilon'$ of the plane $\epsilon$. Now all lines lying in $\epsilon$ are normal to $[xy]$, since their first views fall on the same point $\epsilon'$. $\epsilon$ is thus normal to $[xy]$ and therefore (completely) parallel to $[zt]$. In the second view we see everything in true size! $A''$, $B''$, $C''$ cannot be taken as lying on one line, for otherwise no plane—only the line $ABC$—would result. The equations of a plane normal to $[xy]$ are: $x =$ constant, $y =$ constant.

It is also possible that, for a plane, $A'$ coincides with $A''$, $B'$ with $B''$, and $C'$ with $C''$. Then all the views for all points coincide and we have to do with the so-called coincidence plane, or base plane, with the equations $x + z = 0$, $y + t = 0$. Then, as we can readily see from the line construction, the length of a line in the coincidence plane is equal to the product of $\sqrt{2}$ and the lengths of lines in the view. Therefore, the view of a figure in the coincidence plane reproduces this figure similarly reduced in the proportion $\sqrt{2} : 1$.

## 15. THE POINT OF INTERSECTION
## OF TWO PLANES

Let a plane $\epsilon$ be represented by the triangle $ABC$, and a plane $\varphi$ by the triangle $DEF$ in the first and second views (Figure 13). The auxiliary views, which are useful for the practical construction, are left out. If the point of intersection is $S$, then $S'$ must lie in such a manner that when we look for its second views in both planes, they must coincide in a single point $S''$ and vice versa.

We overlay the first views with a group of parallel lines equally spaced, for instance in the direction of $A'C'$. Then these lines shall be the first view of lines in $\epsilon(g_1 g_2 g_3 g_4 \ldots)$ as well as the first views of lines in $\varphi(h_1 h_2 h_3 h_4 \ldots)$. Then we seek the second views, for all of them, $g_1'' g_2'' \ldots$ in $\epsilon''$ and $h_1'' h_2'' \ldots$ in $\varphi''$; both these groups are likewise evenly spaced parallels, thence, the points of intersection $g_1''$ with $h_1''$ and $g_2''$ with $h_2''$ etc. lie on a line which is designated $a''$ with respect to $\epsilon$ and $b''$ with respect

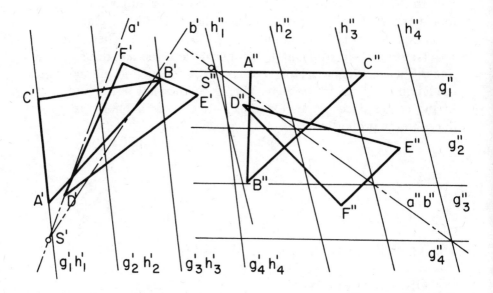

FIGURE 13

to $\varphi$. If $S'$ were to lie on one of the lines $g'h'$, then both second views with respect to $\epsilon$ and $\varphi$ would have to lie on $g''$ and $h''$. Hence, if $S$ should have a concurring second view, then $S''$ must lie at the point of intersection of a $g''$ with the $h''$ which belongs to it and therefore on the line $a''b''$. If we now look for $a'$ in $\epsilon'$ and $b'$ in $\varphi'$, then $a'$, $b'$ intersect in the first view $S'$ of the point of intersection we are seeking. If we now seek for $S'$ the second view for both planes, then we arrive at the same point $S''$.

A discussion of this construction would also produce the possible special positions of both planes relative to each other, if, for example, the cluster $(g'')$ is parallel to $(h'')$, if $a' \parallel b'$, or

$a'$ coincides with $b'$, etc. However, we want to leave it in the general case.

Look for the point of intersection of a plane with the coincidence plane, or with a half-projecting plane (using the auxiliary views).

# 16. ASSUMPTION OF PARTICULAR POSITIONS

# OF PLANES WITH RESPECT

# TO EACH OTHER

We assume $\epsilon$ as given by the two intersecting lines $a$ and $b$, and $\varphi$ given by the intersecting lines $e$ and $f$. If, for example, $a$ coincides with $e$, then $\epsilon$ and $\varphi$ intersect along this line; $\epsilon$ and $\varphi$ and the lines $a \equiv e$, $f$ lie in one space. If $a$ is parallel to $e$, $b$ and $f$ lying arbitrarily, then $\epsilon$ and $\varphi$ have in common an infinitely distant point, namely the point of intersection of $a$ and $e$; they are semi-parallel. But if $a \parallel e$ and $b \parallel f$, then the planes have in common two points and consequently a line at an infinite location, and are parallel. We see that in semi-parallel planes there is only one direction of lines in a plane that is parallel to a direction of lines in a plane that is parallel to a direction of lines in another. In parallel planes, to the contrary, to an arbitrary line in one plane there are always parallels in the other.

These different positions of two planes are to be assumed when each is determined by a triangle. Through a point, one plane can be placed parallel to another plane.

## 17. A THEOREM FOR THREE PLANES

Given are three planes, $\epsilon_1$ $\epsilon_2$ $\epsilon_3$; the point of intersection of $\epsilon_1$ with $\epsilon_2$ is called $P_{12}$; similarly, the other possible points of intersection would be called $P_{23}$ and $P_{31}$. Through these three points a single plane $\epsilon$ now passes. Now, for example, since $P_{12}$ and $P_{31}$ lie in $\epsilon_1$ and also in $\epsilon$, plane $\epsilon$ cuts the plane $\epsilon_1$ in a line, also the planes $\epsilon_2$ and $\epsilon_3$. For three planes, there is thus one single plane which cuts all three in lines.

$\epsilon_1$ will be represented by the triangle $P_{12}$, $P_{31}$, $E_1$, where $E_1$ is an arbitrary point of $\epsilon_1$; similarly for $\epsilon_2$ and $\epsilon_3$. Represent the figure of the four planes. What analytical theorem is to be found in this geometrical one?

## 18. REPRESENTATION OF THE SPACE

A space is defined by four points, $A$, $B$, $C$, $D$ in a general position. If we picture these points connected by lines, we obtain a tetrahedron $T$, that plays the same role in the definition of a space that the triangle plays for the plane. Also, a space could be defined by three lines intersecting in a point. In Figure 14 only one of the three views of the tetrahedron is drawn, such as the first **T'**. If we picture all three views **T'**, **T̄**, and **T''**, then we can take **T'** as the plan view and **T̄** as the elevation view of the vertical projection of **T** on **R₃**. That gives a tetrahedron in **R₃**. **T'** is now the projection of this tetrahedron on [*xy*].

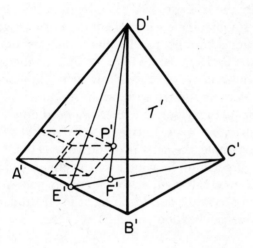

If we consider only one view of figures in space, then we must keep in mind that it has originated from a twofold projection. If we now wish to represent a point *P* in space, then we must connect it firmly to **T**. If we imagine a plane placed through the sides *CD* and *P*, then the plane will cut the side *AB* in a point *E* and *P* lies then in the triangle *CDE*; here another point *F* must originate on *CE*, which is the intersection of *DP* with *CE*. Figure 14 thus shows the structure pertaining to every point *P* with respect to the tetrahedron. If we have two or three points given in this manner, then they determine a line or a plane, respectively, within the space.

If we now desire to make constructions in the space given by **T**, then we can picture a congruent tetrahedron in **R₃** con-

structed from the six lateral edges, in which the desired construction is accomplished stereometrically and the resulting
points are projected back. Since we cannot, of course, work
directly in $R_3$, it is recommended that we work in a plan and
elevation view in an auxiliary figure, in which case we picture,
for example, the triangle $ABC$ to be lying in the plan view. We
must also establish the six lateral edges in true length and from
this construct a tetrahedron in plan and elevation views. By
means of line projections, we relate to this tetrahedron all given
points. To this end, it is good to draw every point on the oblique
parallel coordinate system with origin $A$ and axes $AB$, $AC$, $AD$,
as it is indicated in Figure 14; then we need only to work with
lines on these three axes. In this way, we should be able to construct, for example, the perpendicular from $D$ to the plane $ABC$.
This entire procedure, by which we imagine the space brought
into $R_3$, is rather involved, as we can easily convince ourselves
by actually carrying it out, but it has the advantage of lending
itself to easy visualization (cf. Figure 17).

How does a space lie in which the first (basic) views
of all points fall on a line? Equation?

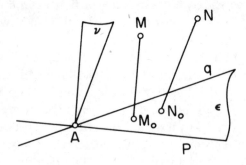

FIGURE 15

Carry out the following exercise here briefly outlined. A plane $\epsilon$ is given by two lines $p$ and $q$ that intersect at $A$; establish at $A$ the plane normal to $\epsilon$. Figure 15 gives an explanatory figure in one view. One takes an arbitrary point $M$ outside $\epsilon$ and constructs, in the space determined by $M$ and $\epsilon$, the perpendicular from $M$ to $\epsilon$ with the base point $M_0$ in the manner given above. Then we take $N$ outside $\epsilon$ a second time, and in this way determine the perpendicular $MN_0$ in the new space lying in $\epsilon$ and $N$. We have now found two normals parallel to $A$, then the sought for normal-plane $v$ is determined by these parallels.

# 19. THE ROTATION OF A SPACE

# AROUND A PLANE

Let a space $\Delta$ be given by a plane $\epsilon$ and the point $P$. In Figure 16, which shows only one view, $\epsilon$ is defined by a parallelogram. Further let us imagine a second space $\Delta_1$, likewise lying through $\epsilon$. If, from $P$, we drop the perpendicular to $\epsilon$ with the base $P_0$ in $\Delta$, then $P_0$ is the projection from $P$ onto $\epsilon$ and $P$ is rigidly fixed to $\epsilon$ by the perpendicular $\overline{PP_0}$. Now picture a further perpendicular to $\epsilon$ erected at $P_0$, but in space $\Delta_1$, and then laid off on it, from $P_0$, the line $\overline{PP_0}$ which produces point $P_1$. The plane $PP_0P_1$ is normal to $\epsilon$ at point $P_0$. If we do this with all points of $\Delta$, then to every $P$ in $\Delta$ belongs a corresponding point $P_1$ in $\Delta_1$.

In the figure this construction is given also for a second point $Q$; we should notice here that the triangles $PP_0P_1$ and $QQ_0Q_1$ have parallel sides, and therefore are similar, so that

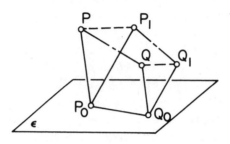

$Q_1$ originates in a simple manner by placing a parallel to $PP_1$ through $Q$. We could, therefore, obtain the points in $\Delta_1$ also in the following manner: we lay the parallel to $PP_1$ through each point of $\Delta$ and look for its point of intersection with $\Delta_1$, or expressed more simply, project point by point the space $\Delta$ parallelwise into space $\Delta_1$, in the direction of $PP_1$. The line $\overline{PQ}$ then becomes the line $\overline{P_1Q_1}$ and both are of equal length. $PP_0$ and $P_1P_0$ must form right angles with $P_0Q_0$; hence the trapezoids $PP_0Q_0Q$ and $P_1P_0Q_0Q_1$ possess three pairs of sides of equal length and with right angles at $P_0$ and $Q_0$, and are thus congruent. By means of this procedure, all images lying in $\Delta$ change to congruent images in $\Delta_1$; only the points of $\epsilon$ remain at rest during this changeover. One says that one has rotated space $\Delta$ around the plane $\epsilon$ lying in it into space $\Delta_1$, and one speaks of the rotation of two spaces into one another about their plane of intersection. The analogy to this in $\mathbf{R}_3$ is the rotation of two planes into one another about their line of intersection. However, through $\epsilon$ go $\infty^1$ spaces, and we can rotate $\Delta$ around $\epsilon$ into all of these, successively. Then all points that $P$ may describe will lie on a plane erected normal to $\epsilon$ at $P_0$. Now, since the distance of the points $P$ from $P_0$ is always the same, the path from $P$ in a complete revolution is a circle. Summarizing we can say: in rotating a space about a plane $\epsilon$ lying within it, all points describe circles which lie in planes that are normal to $\epsilon$ and whose centers are found in $\epsilon$. Thus, there are $\infty^3$ such circular paths.

We can make use of this rotation to bring a space $\Delta$ into our $\boldsymbol{R}_3$. We need only to find the plane of intersection $\epsilon$ of $\Delta$ and $\boldsymbol{R}_3$ and then carry out the construction of the stipulated procedure. We can easily find $\epsilon$ by causing three arbitrary lines of $\Delta$ to intersect $\boldsymbol{R}_3$ and taking $\epsilon$ as fixed by these three points. In the main, we are concerned with the construction of a triangle $PP_0P_1$, for then we can easily find the corresponding triangle for every point; this way, the transition from $\Delta$ to $\boldsymbol{R}_3$ and back is easily effected. In Figure 17 we shall think of $\epsilon$ as already constructed and shall fix it in $\boldsymbol{R}_3$ by the triangle $ABC$. $\Delta$ will then be assumed to be defined by points $A$, $B$; $C$, $P$. Further, to simplify matters, we make the non-essential assumption that two sides of the triangle $ABC$ will be principal lines (in the sense of the plan and elevation view procedure).

First, one determines by construction the true lengths of all six edges of the tetrahedron: using these lengths, one constructs the triangles, $\boldsymbol{ABC}$, $\boldsymbol{ABP}$, and $\boldsymbol{ACP}$ and joins them together into an auxiliary figure on the drawing plane. One pictures the tetrahedron constructed over the triange $\boldsymbol{ABC}$. To this purpose we fold triangle $\boldsymbol{ABC}$ around $\boldsymbol{AB}$ and $\boldsymbol{ACP}$ around $\boldsymbol{AC}$, until both points $\boldsymbol{P}$ join above the drawing plane. The two points $\boldsymbol{P}$ describe circles whose projections on the drawing surface are the normals from the points $\boldsymbol{P}$ on $\boldsymbol{AB}$ and $\boldsymbol{AC}$. Where these normals meet is the projection of the fourth tetrahedron point $\boldsymbol{P}_0$, which also determines the base of the altitude of the tetrahedron. Now we carry $\boldsymbol{P}_0$ over to the principal figure by means of the indicated parallelogram in the plan and elevation views of $ABC$. $P_0''$ lies on $X$, and in this way the three views of $PP_0$ are obtained. Now, at $P_0$, we erect the perpendicular $n$ to the triangle in $\boldsymbol{R}_3$ and lay off the true length of $\overline{PP_0}$ on $n$ from $P_0$, by which we obtain $P_1$ (all by ordinary descriptive geometry). Now the characteristic triangle is given for one point in all three views. If we want to get to $Q_1$ from another point $Q$ of $\Delta$, then we have only to lay the parallel to $PP_1$ through $Q$ and look for the intersection

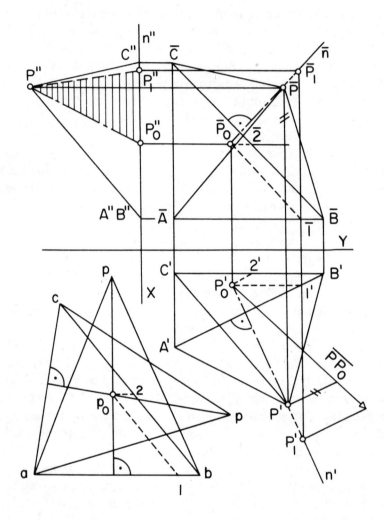

FIGURE 17

with $\boldsymbol{R}_3$ (in the second view the point of intersection with $X$). If, however, $Q_1$ is given in $\boldsymbol{R}_3$, then we must drop the perpendicular to $\epsilon$ (parallel to $P_1P_0$), find the base ($Q_0$) and draw above the line obtained a triangle parallel to the characteristic triangle of $P$.

Why does the characteristic triangle in the first view and in the auxiliary view appear as lines?

## 20. REPRESENTATION OF THE TRACES

## OF A SPACE

If a space $\Delta$ is denoted by the equation

$$ax + by + cz + dt + e = 0$$

then we obtain its line of intersection $d_1$ with $[xy]$ through the condition $z = t = 0$. We call $d_1$ the first trace, the line of intersection $d_3$ with $[zt]$ the third trace, and finally the line of intersection $d_2$ with $[yz]$ the second or auxiliary trace. The equations of these three traces are:

$$d_1 : ax + by + e = 0$$
$$d_2 : by + cz + e = 0$$
$$d_3 : cz + dt + e = 0.$$

We recognize the fact that these traces intersect in the axes; in Figure 18 they are represented in all three views. To abbreviate, we write the notations $d_1$, $d_2$, $d_3$ for $d_1'$, $d_2$, $d_3''$ and remember that these traces together with the coordinate planes in which they lie, have been brought into the drawing planes.

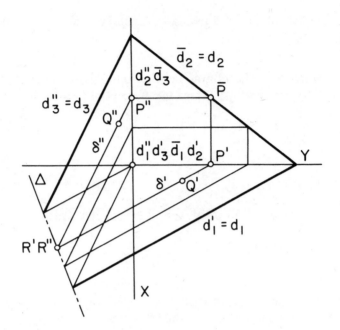

$$\overline{d}_2 = d_2$$

FIGURE 18

Assume spacial positions of the traces (parallel to the axes), look for the corresponding equations and give the location of the spaces. What traces does space $t' = $ constant have?

A plane $\epsilon$ in $\Delta$ must have its trace-points $E_1$, $E_2$, $E_3$ on the respective traces, $d_1$, $d_2$, $d_3$. A plane within $\Delta$ can, therefore, easily be determined by its trace-points. If two spaces $\Delta(d_1d_2d_3)$ and $\Lambda(l_1l_2l_3)$ are given by their traces, then their intersection plane $\epsilon$ can easily be specified by the trace-points $E_1$, $E_2$, $E_3$, since $E_i$ must be the point of intersection of $d_i$ with $l_i$: ($i = 1, 2, 3$).

Represent the traces of a space defined by four points. We must find the trace-points of two planes and connect the corresponding trace-points. How do the traces of parallel spaces lie?

We now inquire about all points of $\Delta$, the first views of which lie on a line $v'$ which is parallel to $d_1$. Such a point would be $P'$ in the intersection of $v'$ with $Y$; we shall imagine the corresponding point $P$ as lying on the second trace $d_2$, so that $\overline{P}$ comes to lie on $d_2$ and $P''$ on $X$. For a point whose first view lies on $v'$, it is seen that:

$$ax + by + f = 0.$$

If we introduce this into the equation of $\Delta$, then we obtain the condition for the second views:

$$cz + dt + (e - f) = 0,$$

i.e. the second views can be taken arbitrarily on a line $v''$ that is parallel to $d_3$. Because a point $P''$ is already known, we need only to lay line $v''$ parallel to trace $d_3$ through $P''$. In this way, a definite line $v''$ always belongs to line $v'$, and vice versa; if we take an arbitrary point $Q'$ on $v'$ as the first view, and an arbitrary point $Q''$ on $v''$ as the second view of a point $Q$, then $Q$ always lies in space $\Delta$. There are $\infty^2$ points whose views fall on the corresponding lines $v'$, $v''$; they therefore lie in a double-projecting plane and $v'$ and $v''$ are their views. There are $\infty^1$ such planes in $\Delta$, since we can draw $\infty^1 v'$'s parallel to $d_1$. In Figure 18, a few are drawn and we see that when $v'$ falls on $d_3$, $v''$ passes through $O$; also, if $v''$ falls on $d_3$, $v'$ likewise goes through $O$.

Where $v'$ and $v''$ intersect, there lie the coincident views of a point $R$; this point must be a point on the coincidence plane. If we look for the point of intersection for all associated rays $v'$, $v''$, these will all be found on a line that we denote with the letter of the space $\Delta$; it must be a line, since it represents the coincident views of the line of intersection of space with the coincidence plane. Its equation we obtain in the $[xy]$ system from the equation of space, if we set $z = -x$ and $t = -y$:

$$(a - c)x + (b - d)y + e = 0.$$

We call all lines parallel to $\nu'$ the first defining ray bundle; all lines parallel to $\nu''$ we call the second defining ray bundle, and $\Delta$ we call the axis of space.

# 21. THE REPRESENTATION OF SPACE

# BY THE DEFINING RAY BUNDLE

# (GROUP OF PROJECTION LINES)

A space $\Delta$ is defined by giving its axis and two defining rays $\nu'$, $\nu''$ (Figure 19), which we can easily find either from the traces or the equation for the space. The views of a space point $P$ can lie only such that a first projection line through $P'$ and a second through $P''$ meet on the axis. If we assume that both bundles are normal to the axis, then we arrive at the same condition as that which holds for the plane and elevation views of the customary space $\mathbf{R}_3$. A line $g$ in $\Delta$ is determined by arbitrary views $g'$, $g''$, since the ray bundles (or groups of projection lines) denote the relationships between the points in the views ($P$ and $Q$ in the figure). We can now easily locate arbitrary spaces through a given line fixed by two points $P$ and $Q$. We place parallels through $P''$ and $Q''$ (2nd bundle), and through $P'$ and $Q'$ as well (1st bundle); the locations where the lines through $P''$ and $P'$ intersect, and also those through $Q''$ and $Q'$, represent two points on the axis of the space.

A plane in space can be considered as defined by triangle $ABC$ (Figure 19). If we want to find the point of intersection $S$ of $g$ with the triangle $ABC$, then $S''$ must lie on $g''$, $S'$ on $g'$; and, further, $S$ must lie in $ABC$. If we interpret $g''$ as the second view $h''$ of a line in the triangle, then $h'$ is easily determined from it; the point of intersection of $g'$ with $h'$ is already $S'$. This construction is just the same as the corresponding one in the plan and elevation procedures. Now we can place a space through a plane. If the plane is given by the view of the triangle $A'B'C'$ and $A''B''C''$, then we can, for example, lay three arbitrary parallels through $A'B'$ and $C'$. If the line through $C'$ intersects the side $A'B'$ in point $D'$, then we have to look for $D''$ on $A''B''$ in the second view, and the direction of the second defining ray bundle, or group of projection lines, is determined by $C''D''$.

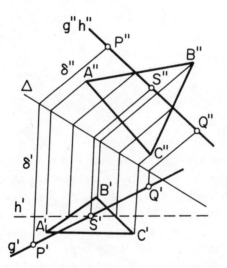

Figure 19

To find the intersecting plane of two spaces $\Delta(\Delta,\ \nu',\ \nu'')$ and $\Lambda(\Lambda,\ \lambda',\ \lambda'')$ means to locate three points on it (Figure 20). If we chose, for example, $A''$ arbitrarily and if $A$ must be in both spaces at the same time, then we must place through $A''$ a second line of projection $\Delta$ and one from $\Lambda$, find the corresponding first ordering lines and bring them to intersect ($A'$). By performing this construction three times, we obtain three points on the desired intersection plane. This represents also a simple construction method for the completion of two fields of affinity.

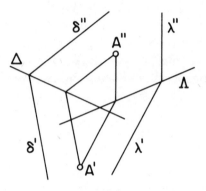

FIGURE 20

If we are looking for the intersection of line $g$ with a space $\Delta$, then we locate an arbitrary space $\Lambda$ through $g$. The spaces $\Lambda$ and $\Delta$ intersect in a plane $\epsilon$. Since $\epsilon$ and $g$ now lie in $\Lambda$, they have a point of intersection which now also lies in $\Delta$.

The intersection of a plane $\epsilon$ with a space $\Delta$ is found by placing an auxiliary space $\Lambda$ through $\epsilon$ and causing it to intersect with $\Delta$, whereby the plane $\psi$ is formed. Since $\epsilon$ and $\psi$ lie in $\Lambda$, they have an intersection line which also lies in $\Delta$.

The intersection of two planes $\epsilon$ and $\varphi$ can be handled as follows: we place the auxiliary space $\Delta$ through $\epsilon$ and the auxiliary space $\Lambda$ through $\varphi$, and have them intersect; this produces the plane $\psi$. Because $\epsilon$ and $\psi$ lie in $\Delta$, they have a line of intersection $g$. $\varphi$ and $\psi$ have the line of intersection $h$. The point of intersection of $g$ and $h$, which of course lie in $\psi$, is the desired point.

By representing space through the parallel ray bundles (or sheaves of projection lines), we have found a very simple method for solving all position problems in $R_4$. The auxiliary views were not at all needed.

Please actually carry out the given exercises.

## 22. THE NORMALS TO A SPACE

Of the metric problems, we want to treat only one by graphic construction, namely that of a line which is normal to a space. We know that a normal to $R_3$ is parallel to the axis $[t]$ and to every other line that is parallel to $[t]$. Since every arbitrary space can be brought into $R_3$ by rotation, a normal validly fixed to such a space will come to lie in the direction $[t]$. Therefore, we can attribute to every space that which we already know about $R_3$; a line is normal to a space if it is normal to three lines lying in the space and passed through their point of intersection; then of course it forms a right angle with every straight line drawn through the point of intersection in the space. If we drop a perpendicular from a point to the space, then this is the shortest connection line between the point and any point of the space. We want to drop a perpendicular from a point $P$ to a space $\Delta$ determined by the ray bundle, or sheaf of projection lines (Figure 21).

First we seek a point $Q$, which lies in a double-projecting plane $\nu$ and where the length of line $\overline{PQ}$ becomes a minimum. Therefore, we must take $Q''$ on $\nu''$ and the point $Q'$ on $\nu'$ in such a way that $\overline{P'Q'^2} + \overline{P''Q''^2}$ will be as small as possible. This is then,

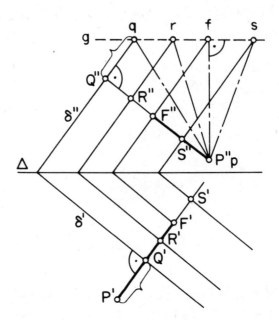

FIGURE 21

obviously, the case when $Q'$ is the base of the perpendicular from $P'$ to $\nu'$; as it is for $Q''$. If we take additional groups of ray bundles (parallel projection lines), then we will get in the thus determined double-projecting planes the points $R, S, \ldots$, which in this plane are always the points closest to $P$. Consequently we have the line lengths $\overline{PQ}, \overline{PR}, \overline{PS}. \ldots$ Among these lines must exist a shortest $\overline{PF}$. For this purpose we determine the true lengths of the lines $\overline{PQ}, \overline{PR}, \overline{PS}, \ldots$, by using the second views directly as legs or short sides of the line construction. It is thus that we obtain the true lengths $PQ, PR, PS, \ldots$ Now we can easily understand that, for this construction, points $Q, R, S, \ldots$ lie on a line $g$. The point $F$ lying on $g$ must have the shortest distance from $P$; one must drop the perpendicular from $P$ to $g$, and obtain thus the true length of the perpendicular $\overline{PS}$.

Reversal of the line construction procedure yields $F''$ and $F'$ as views of the desired base point.

The first view of a normal to the space is normal to a line $v'$, hence also normal to the first trace. Similarly, the second view is normal to the third trace, and finally the auxiliary view is normal to the second trace. We can, therefore, simply erect the perpendicular $n$ at a point $P$ on space $\Delta$, represented by traces $d_1$, $d_2$, $d_3$, (Figure 22); this perpendicular $n$ can be immediately identified by all three views.

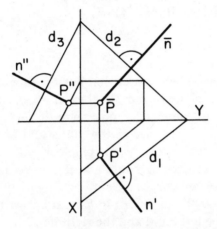

FIGURE 22

Construct in a point of a plane the plane normal to it. Erect the space normal to a point on a line. How large are the distances of a point from the coordinate spaces?

In the same way as with right angles, we can work with arbitrary angles in $R_4$. We merely want to point out that we conceive of the angle of a space $\Delta$ with the space $\Lambda$ as the measure of the rotation which we must perform, in order to bring $\Delta$ around the common plane toward $\Lambda$. The angle will be denoted by the arc which a point from Δ describes in rotating to Λ.

How large is the angle of the space, given in Figure 17, with $R_3$?

## 23. $R_4$ IN RELATION TO $R_3$

When we have two figures that possess mirror-image symmetry lying in a plane of our $R_3$, they are congruent but they cannot be made to coincide by movement in the plane. For this, we must lift one figure out of the plane and only through a movement in $R_3$ can it then be made to coincide with the other figure. There is something similar to this in $R_3$ in the case of bodies possessing mirror-image symmetry which can be made to coincide only by a movement in $R_4$, but not within $R_3$; let us think, e.g., of the left hand and the right hand.

Let us imagine a plane $ABC$ in $R_3$ and the perpendicular in $C$ on which are the mirror-image points $D$, $D_1$ (Figure 23). Then the tetrahedra $ABCD$ and $ABCD_1$ are indeed congruent, but not coincident. If we now picture $R_3$ rotated around the plane $ABC$, then $D$ describes a circular path outside $R_3$, hence in $R_4$. To be sure, after a half revolution point $D$ returns to $R_3$, to position $D_1$, since $\overline{CD}$ as well as $\overline{CD_1}$ are radii of the circle of revolution. Now, by a movement in $R_4$, the tetrahedra, possessing mirror-image symmetry, have been made to coincide— of course, only by imagination.

Let us imagine situated in $R_3$, a body $K_1$ which lies entirely within another body $K_2$. Then it will not be possible to take $K_1$

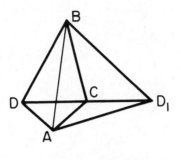

FIGURE 23

out of $K_2$ without breaking the surfaces of $K_2$. But with the help of $R_4$, this can be done. We need only shift $K_1$ somehow parallel into $R_4$; then no point of the surface of $K_1$ can collide with a point on the surface of $K_2$, since $K_2$ remains in $R_3$. Thereby, $K_1$ has been taken out of $K_2$ and can now again be brought into $R_3$ next to $K_2$. But of course, this transformation cannot be performed physically.

To the same category belongs the problem of untying a closed knot in $R_3$ (Figure 24), without cutting it. With the help of $R_4$ this is easy. How?

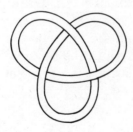

FIGURE 24

## 24. THE POLYTOPES (MULTICELLS)

These are the bodies of $R_4$ which are analogous to the bodies of $\mathbf{R}_3$. If we have an arbitrary space $R_3$ somehow bordered by surfaces, then we call this position of space, as in $\mathbf{R}_3$, a body. If we now move this body a distance in $R_4$, whereby the shape and size of the body may also be changeable, a certain part of $R_4$ will be contacted, and the totality of all of these points will form a part of $R_4$. One designates a portion of $R_4$, which can be bordered or confined by common plane-surfaced bodies, as a polytope or multicell. The simplest polytope is the "simplex (five-cell or basic angular body).

A simplex is denoted by five points of $R_4$, namely, $A$, $B$, $C$, $D$, $E$; it is thus the extension of the concept of a triangle on the plane and a tetrahedron in space. In Figure 25 one of three views is drawn. The ten possible lines connecting the given points are called the edges. Let us remember how Figure 25 originates. If we project the simplex from $R_4$ onto $\mathbf{R}_3$, we obtain five points in $\mathbf{R}_3$ with all possible connecting lines. The problem may be thought of in this way: the projections of $A$, $B$, $C$, $D$ form a tetrahedron and the projection of $E$ is a point on the inside of the tetrahedron. In the same manner, the projection of a tetrahedron on a surface is a figure of four points (see the smaller drawing of Figure 25). From this we should be able to establish a simple space model of the projection of a simplex onto our $\mathbf{R}_3$. The drawing in Figure 25 is, further, a new projection of this model onto a plane. The five points determine two triangles and five tetrahedra. We say that the simplex is bordered by the tetrahedra *ABCD*, *ABCE*, *BCDE*, *ACDE*, and

*ABDE*, each of these again by four triangles, whereby each two tetrahedra always have a triangle in common; each triangle is bordered by three edges whereby each edge belongs to three triangles. Figure 25 permits these relationships to be read off, without of course being able to allow a bona fide mental perception. The thing is, that we can arrive at conclusions regarding the polytope in the same manner as we can arrive at conclusions regarding a body from its projection onto a plane.

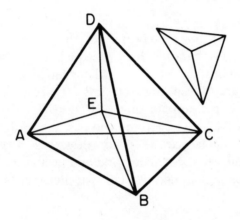

FIGURE 25

If all six edges are of equal length, then we call it a regular simplex. One can for example take a regular tetrahedron in $R_3$ with the edge length $a$, and ask for the point in $R_4$ which is at a distance $a$ from all four corner points; this is the same as the solution of four equations. The point so found is the fifth corner point of the regular simplex. It is bounded by five regular tetrahedra.

Imagine, in the [xy] plane, an equilateral triangle $A(0, 0)$, $B(2, 0)$, $C(1, \sqrt{3})$ and upon it construct a regular tetrahedron and, further, a regular simplex. Compute the coordinates of the corner point; represent the polytope.

If we have a polyhedron in an $R_3$ and connect with lines all its corner points to a point $S$ lying outside, then we obtain a (four-dimensional) pyramid. This is bounded by the polyhedron and just by common pyramids. Such a bounding pyramid originates simply by connecting $S$ with the corners of a bounding polygon of the polyhedron. If the polyhedron is a tetrahedron then we obtain the simplex.

Draw a pyramid that originates from a cube as "basic form."

If we imagine a body moved parallel in $R_4$ so that each point describes parallel lines of equal length, then a (four-dimensional) prism develops. If the given body was a parallelepiped, the prism resulting from it is called a parallelotope. Figure 26 shows a picture of this. $ABCDEFGH$ is the starting position, and $A_1B_1C_1, \ldots, H_1$, the end position of the body. By this movement, each parallelogram describes a parallelepiped; added to this are the starting and end positions. Consequently, the polytope is bounded by eight parallelepipeds.

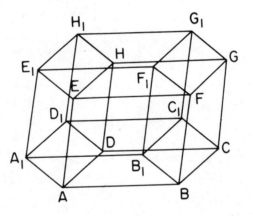

FIGURE 26

If the parallelepiped is a cube $AB$ . . . , and if, moreover, $AA_1$ is perpendicular to the space of the cube, and if $AA_1$ is of the same length as the side of the cube, then we obtain a regular polytope, the eight-cell, which is bounded by eight cubes.

The regular eight-cell of simplest position is given by the origin and the unit points on the coordinate axes. Then the coordinates of the 16 corner points are:

| | | | |
|---|---|---|---|
| $A(0\ 0\ 0\ 0)$ | $E(0\ 0\ 1\ 0)$ | $A_1(0\ 0\ 0\ 1)$ | $E_1(0\ 0\ 1\ 1)$ |
| $B(1\ 0\ 0\ 0)$ | $F(1\ 0\ 1\ 0)$ | $B_1(1\ 0\ 0\ 1)$ | $F_1(1\ 0\ 1\ 1)$ |
| $C(1\ 1\ 0\ 0)$ | $G(1\ 1\ 1\ 0)$ | $C_1(1\ 1\ 0\ 1)$ | $G_1(1\ 1\ 1\ 1)$ |
| $D(0\ 1\ 0\ 0)$ | $H(0\ 1\ 1\ 0)$ | $D_1(0\ 1\ 0\ 1)$ | $H_1(0\ 1\ 1\ 1)$. |

This polytope is also called the polytope of measure, because it serves as a unit of $R_4$-volume. If we were using the *cm* as unit of length, the unit of volume in $R_4$ would be denoted by $cm^4$.

## 25. THE SUPER SPHERE

### (SPHERE IN FOUR-DIMENSIONAL SPACE)

Of the curved structures, we want to consider only one which is defined as follows: we want to find the geometrical locus of all points $P(xyzt)$ which are a distance $r$ from the fixed point $M(x_0y_0z_0t_0)$. The equation for this, according to the distance formula, is

$$(x - x_0)^2 + (y - y_0)^2 + (z - z_0)^2 + (t - t_0)^2 = r^2.$$

The body is thus a quadratic three-dimensional space $V_3^2$ and is called a sphere, with $M$ as the center, $r$ as the radius. As an example of a curved space, the sphere is the analog to the circle on the plane and the ball in space. We want to represent them, if $M$ (by views) and $r$ are given (Figure 27). For a point $P$ of the sphere we have in the figures $P'M'^2 + P''M''^2 = r^2$. Thus if

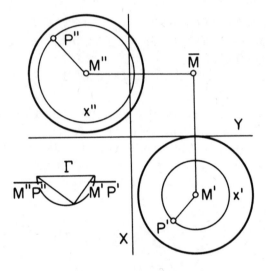

FIGURE 27

$P'$ is assumed for example, then only the distance from $M$ is determined for the second view; thus $P''$ can lie on a circle $x''$. Conversely, for every point of $x''$ as a first view, there belongs an arbitrary point on the circle $x'$ through $P'$. Thus, a first arbitrary view of a point can be taken on $x'$, and a second arbitrary view of a point can be taken on $x''$, and these determine a point of the sphere. In this manner, a definite corresponding circle about $M''$ thus goes with a definite circle about $M'$, and conversely. The views of the points on the sphere are thus divided into two systems of concentric circles; similarly as in linear space the views were distributed on two sheaves of parallel rays. If $x'$ becomes a point, then the radius of $x''$ takes on its greatest value, namely $r$, and conversely. Thus, the first and second views of all points lie within two circles of radius $r$, because of which these circles are called contours. In the auxiliary figure there is also such a contour circle.

If we cut the sphere with $\textbf{R}_3$, then we must put $t = 0$ into its equation and obtain the sphere

$$(x - x_0)^2 + (y - y_0)^2 + (z - z_0)^2 = r^2 - t_0{}^2.$$

$\textbf{R}_3$, and thus every space, cuts a super-sphere according to a sphere, if intersection takes place at all. If the sphere of intersection shrinks down to a point, we say that the space touches the sphere at this place; the space is then normal to the radius of the point of contact.

Construct the spherical intersection of a sphere with $\textbf{R}_3$. Place the contacting space onto the sphere in $P$ and determine its traces.

## 26. LINES IN R$_4$

If we assume three equations governing the coordinates $x$, $y$, $z$, $t$, which, however, shall not all be linear, then the one-dimensional locus thus determined can no longer be a line. We then speak of a curve $k$ in $R_4$. A curve can, of course, also lie in $R_3$ or $R_2$; if so, then there must be one or two linear equations either among the three equations or derivable from them. From the three equations we can, for example, compute $x$, $y$, $z$, and obtain as functions of $t$:

$$x = \varphi\,(t),\, y = \psi\,(t),\, z = \chi\,(t).$$

If we assume all possible values for $t$, then we obtain all points of the curve $k$. The views may easily be drawn (Figure 28). $z = \chi\,(t)$ is already the equation for $k''$. The equation for $k'$ we obtain from $x = \varphi$, $y = \psi$, by elimination of $t$, and in the same way that for $k$. The connection between the points of the three

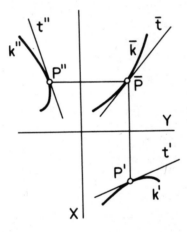

FIGURE 28

curves in the views takes place through the projection lines. We define a tangent $t$ in $P$, as that line which has two points of arbitrary proximity in common with $k$. The views of a tangent are thus tangents in the corresponding points of the curve in the view. We recall that $k'$ and $\bar{k}$ may be regarded as plan and elevation views of a curve in $\mathbf{R}_3$, which is formed by orthogonal projection of $\bar{k}$ onto $\mathbf{R}_3$. This projected curve is determined by the three given equations, if $t$ is considered as a parameter.

## 27. THE EINSTEIN-MINKOWSKI WORLD

In physics, we can completely define the motion of a material space point $P_0$ in $\textbf{R}_3$ if we know the separate positions, and for every position, the time when the point occupies it. Because the position of $P_0$ in space is given by the coordinates $x$, $y$, $z$, we must add the time $t$ to obtain a complete description of the motion. We group all four items $x$, $y$, $z$, $t$ together as coordinates of a position of point $P_0$ and then call any group of these four dimensions the "world point" $P$.

The consideration of all phenomena of motion in space is thus a calculation with $x$, $y$, $z$, $t$ and hence, working in abstract $R_4$. If for the representation of all "world points" $P$, we again use our descriptive geometry, then we can follow all phenomena of motion by means of graphic construction. A "world point" $P$ (Figure 7) must be denoted by the three views; the corresponding point $P_0$ in $\textbf{R}_3$ has $P_0' = P'$ in the plan view and $\overline{P}_0 = \overline{P}$ in the elevation, and is thus the projection of the "world point" on $\textbf{R}_3$. We can also imagine the views of a "world point" as so originated that we first give the positions of the corresponding point of $\textbf{R}_3$ in plan and elevation views, and introduce the time coordinate in an auxiliary view. The $R_4$ of the "world points" is thus an association of space with time. If we draw the position of several points at time $t = 0$, by which we will designate the present moment, then the "world points" coincide with the corresponding points in space; for $t < 0$, we obtain the positions of the past, and for $t > 0$, we obtain the positions of the future.

If a space point $P_0$ describes a curve $k_0$ in $\textbf{R}_3$, then its coordinates can be given as functions of time $t$ as follows:

$$x = \varphi\,(t),\, y = \psi\,(t),\, z = \chi\,(t).$$

By this means, the corresponding "world points" are determined; these points lie on a line $k$ of $R_4$, the so-called "world line" $k$ of point $P_0$. The views of such a "world line" are drawn in Figure 28. Herein, $k'$ and $\overline{k}$ give the specific time relationships. The three views of a "world line" thus completely replace the three equations of movement of a point in $R_3$. If a point is at rest, its position in $R_3$ remains unchanged, while time alone changes. The "world lines" of points at rest are thus parallel to the $[t]$ axis. As an example, we want to draw the "world line" for a horizontal displacement (Figure 29). The $[xy]$ surface may be thought of as horizontal, and this movement of $P_0$ shall

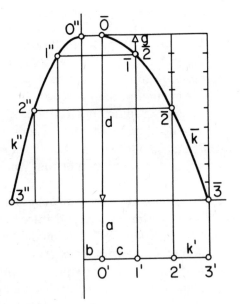

FIGURE 29

extend parallel to the [yz] plane. The equations of this horizontal displacement in **R**₃ are then

$$x = a, y = b + ct, z = d - (g/2)t^2,$$

in which $a$, $b$, $c$, $d$, $g$ are constants. We easily obtain the several positions of the "world points" if we introduce the values 0, 1, 2, . . . for $t$. In Figure 29, the "world points" are denoted with the measures of time, $k'$ is a line parallel to Y; $k$ and $k''$ are parabolas.

Draw the "world line" of a point which moves at uniform rate on a spiral line with vertical axes.

# 28. THE MATERIALIZATION OF $R_4$.

## A SPHERICAL GEOMETRY IN **R**₃

We have, at first, worked abstractly in $R_4$ and then have acquired a closer insight by means of descriptive geometry. Even though it is impossible to attain a direct perception of $R_4$, we have learned to master $R_4$ by means of constructions just as well as we master **R**₃. The question now arises whether it would be possible to visualize directly a geometry in $R_4$ by means of tangible structures. Something of this kind occurred in the preceding section, where the points of $R_4$ were taken as "world points" and were made comprehensible as the displacement of the points in $R_3$; thus we had a visualization of $R_4$ by means of kinematics.

We can however, already visualize $R_4$ in a plane. We take a coordinate system $[xy]$ in the plane and assume that the element of our geometry in this plane is not the point but the point pair; i.e., two points $P'(x_1y_1)$ and $P''(x_2y_2)$ will always be seen in tandem. The pair of points $P'P''$ is thus the "point" of this new geometry. Working with pairs of points is, analytically, calculation with $x_1y_1x_2y_2$, thus with four variables. The geometry of pairs of points on the plane is thus a four-dimensional geometry and we can transfer all theorems of $R_4$ to theorems about point pairs. We have already done this in large measure when we worked with the first and second views of an abstract $R_4$-point. For this purpose, we only need to state

$$x_1 = x, \; y_1 = y, \; x_2 = -z, \; y_2 = -t,$$

and we have the representation of the abstract point $P(xyzt)$ by the pair of points $P'(x_1y_1)$, $P''(x_2y_2)$, which illustrates exactly what has been discussed. We must take into consideration that the views of $P$, namely $P'(xy)$ and $P''(zt)$, were expressed on two coordinate system $[xy]$ and $[zt]$, which coincide but are oriented opposite to each other, while the same points $P'(x_1y_1)$, $P''(x_2y_2)$ are now expressed on a system $[xy]$. Therefore, working with the two views in nothing else but the representation of abstract $R_4$ by the pair of points in the drawing plane. A plane of $R_4$ is in this manner transposed into an affinity, etc.

One can render $R_4$ perceptible by structures of $\boldsymbol{R}_3$ also in a simple manner. Each sphere of $\boldsymbol{R}_3$ is given by the three coordinates $x$, $y$, $z$, of the center and by the radius $t$; thus all the spheres are functions of four variables. If we now consider the sphere as a basic element, namely as "point" with coordinates $(x, y, z, t)$, then each point $P(xyzt)$ of $R_4$ is illustrated by a sphere with center $(xyz)$ and the radius $t$. If we now calculate with the four quantities, then we get relationships for spheres, and we call a geometry in which the sphere plays the role of the basic element a "spherical geometry." $R_4$ is thus rendered perceptible by a spherical geometry. The spaces, planes and lines of $R_4$ then define certain spherical structures which must be examined further.

From the few examples we perceive that those suitable for an illustration of $R_4$ are all the geometric constructions which are defined by four independent variables (their coordinates). If one has once and for all developed an abstract geometry of $R_4$, primarily by examination of the relationships between systems of linear equations, then one needs only to apply the analytical theorems, expressed in geometrical form, to the respective geometry, in which the role of a basic geometric element is played by a structure defined by four numbers (or which is a function of four independent variables).

> Can we also represent $R_4$ on all lines of $\boldsymbol{R}_3$? (Linear or projective geometry.) What is the appearance of the representation of the points of $R_4$ on the sphere of $\boldsymbol{R}_3$ a step lower? (Depicting the points of $\boldsymbol{R}_3$ on the circle of the plane—cyclography.)

## 29. HISTORICAL NOTES

Already at the beginning of the 19th century considerations of spaces of more than three dimensions were making themselves noticeable in different localities, the result of several investigations. But H. Grassman was the first to develop systematically the abstract geometry of several dimensions in his *Ausdehnungslehre* (Theory of Expansion) of 1844. To J. Plucker we owe the concept that we can handle a geometry of several dimensions working with real structures if we only take into account the number of parameters on which the structure depends. Besides these two Germans, we must mention the Italian G. Veronese, who, for the first time in 1881, developed the theory of $R_n$ purely geometrically, especially with regard to the geometry of position. Today the widely developed geometry of several dimensions has become the common property of mathematicians.

## 30. BIBLIOGRAPHICAL NOTE

For further study is recommended the work by P. H. Schoute, *Mehrdimensionale Geometrie* (The Geometry of Several Dimensions) (Part I: Linear Spaces; Part II: The Polytopes), from the Schubert collection Bd. 35 and 36, published by G. Goschen, Leipzig 1902 and 1905. The present book will prepare the reader to follow with understanding the presentations of this work, presentations which are not always simple. A general survey of the present state of the subject is given in the *Encyclopedia of Mathematical Science*, Bd. III, C. 7, in the article by C. Segre: "Mehrdimensionale Raüme" (Spaces of Several Dimensions), where the extremely large amount of literature on the subject is also listed. An introduction to the descriptive geometry of many varieties of space of several dimensions is given in the booklet: L. Eckhart, *Konstructive Abbildungsverfahren* (Constructive Procedures in Representation) published by J. Springer, Vienna, 1926.